LogicWorks

LogicWorks™

INTERACTIVE CIRCUIT DESIGN SOFTWARE

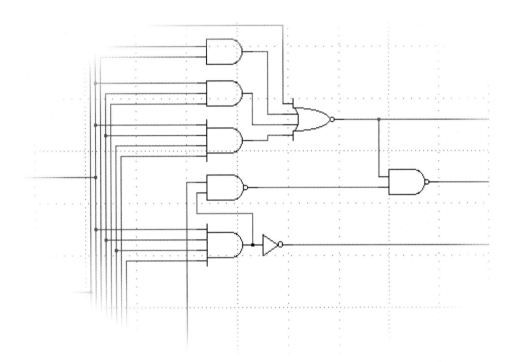

Capilano Computing Systems, Ltd.

The Benjamin/Cummings Publishing Company, Inc.

Redwood City, California • Menlo Park, California
Reading, Massachusetts • New York • Don Mills, Ontario
Wokingham, U.K. • Amsterdam • Bonn • Sydney
Singapore • Tokyo • Madrid • San Juan

Executive Editor: Dan Joraanstad
Sponsoring Editor: Jennifer Young
Editorial Assistant: Laura Cheu
Marketing Manager: Mary Tudor
Production Manager: Gary Palmatier
Text and Cover Design: Gary Palmatier
Copyeditor: Julie Voss
Proofreader: Elizabeth von Radics
Illustrations: Capilano Computing
Composition: Ideas to Images
Film: Just Your Type
Cover Printer: New England Book Components, Inc.
Text Printer and Binder: R. R. Donnelley & Sons
Senior Manufacturing Coordinator: Merry Free Osborn

Library of Congress Cataloging-in-Publication Data

LogicWorks [computer file] : circuit design tools. — [Version] 1.0.0 DOS.
    1 computer disk : 3 1/2 in. + 1 manual.
       System requirements: IBM-compatible PC with 80286 or greater microprocessor; 4MB RAM; DOS 3.1 or greater; monochrome or color monitor with CGA, VGA (preferred) or Hercules graphics card; hard disk with at least 2MB free space; floppy disk drive; printer optional.
    Title from disk label.
    "The LogicWorks schematic and simulation system from Capilano Computing was designed by Chris Dewhurst and coded by Chris Dewhurst, David Taylor, and Ray Quon."—Title screen.
    Student version of DesignWorks.
    Audience: University and college students.
    Issued also for the Macintosh.
    Summary: An integrated schematic diagram and simulation program which allows students to design and test logic circuits. Upwardly compatible with Capilano Computing's DesignWorks professional circuit design system.
    ISBN 0-8053-1310-9 (set). — ISBN 0-201-91503-0 (program disk)
    1. Logic circuits—Design and construction—Software. 2. Logic design—Software.
    3. Computer-aided design—Software. I. Capilano Computing, Limited. II. DesignWorks.
    TK7868.L6 <MRCRR>
    621.39—dc12
       93-27595
       CIP

2 3 4 5 6 7 8 9 10 — DO — 97 96 95 94

The Benjamin/Cummings Publishing Company, Inc.
390 Bridge Parkway
Redwood City, California 94065

Contents

4 User Interface   53

5 Creating the Schematic 61

6 Signals 71

7 Devices 85

8 Simulation   95

9 PROM and PLA Devices   115

10 Primitive Devices   135

11 Menu Reference   151

12 The Device Editor   177

13 Creating Text Reports   191

14 The Parts Window 203

Appendix 207

Preface

Welcome to the exciting world of interactive circuit design. As electronic systems have become more complex, operating speeds higher, and custom chip technology more widespread, software tools for engineers have become an essential part of the design process. It is no longer possible for an individual engineer or a corporation to remain competitive using pencil and paper for design. Powerful computer-aided design (CAD) programs have been commercially developed to meet the increasing demands facing industry. At Capilano Computing Systems, Ltd., our leading product, DesignWorks, is used in government, industrial, and academic labs worldwide, providing users with speed, ease of use, and affordability.

Many instructors want to give their students hands-on experience with CAD tools used in industry, but the high cost and complexity of most commercial CAD programs limit their use at academic institutions. In light of this, we developed LogicWorks, the student version of DesignWorks, to be used by students in lab settings and by instructors as an interactive teaching aid. We are proud to announce that a recent survey identified LogicWorks as the single most popular tool for teaching digital logic at universities.

Objectives

LogicWorks was developed with the following goals in mind:

- To give students an introduction to the concepts and practicalities of using CAD tools.

- To provide a "virtual workbench" that allows students to quickly test circuit design ideas and document results.

- To be easy and intuitive to use, so time is not wasted on the details of installing and operating the software.

- To offer the features and interfaces necessary to work with current technologies.

- To provide an upward path to professional design tools used in the industry.

Features

LogicWorks offers students and instructors the ability to:

- Quickly draw general-purpose schematic diagrams, using standard digital and discrete component symbols.

- Create schematics for SPICE-based analog simulators.

- Create custom symbol libraries with the built-in drawing tools.

- Generate simple netlists and bills of materials from the schematic.

- Interactively simulate the digital portions of the circuit, just as if it were built on a real breadboard.

These features, plus full upward compatibility with DesignWorks, makes LogicWorks an open-ended tool that can form the core of an electronics teaching and research environment.

Supplements

LogicWorks Laboratory Manual   Free to adopters of LogicWorks, this manual consists of 12 laboratory exercises and two final projects developed for coursework at the University of Washington and the University of California at Berkeley. To obtain a free copy, please contact your local sales representative and ask for ISBN 0-8053-1313-3.

Acknowledgments

Many people at Capilano Computing and at Benjamin/Cummings Publishing provided invaluable help in bringing this version of LogicWorks to the world. Particular thanks go out to our editor, Jennifer Young, and her assistant, Laura Cheu, at Benjamin/Cummings and to Addam Smith and David Taylor at Capilano, all of whom remained cheerful and fun to work with despite setbacks and schedule pressures.

Other key contributors include our previous editor, Lisa Moller; our marketing manager, Mary Tudor; Neil MacKenzie and Angela Der at Capilano; and Gary Palmatier at Ideas to Images.

Special thanks go out to Gaetano Borriello and Carl Ebeling at the University of Washington and to Randy Katz, author of *Contemporary Logic Design* (Benjamin/Cummings), for their contributions to the laboratory manual and to Don Joy at Sonoma State University for reviewing these labs. We would also like to acknowledge our many friends and supporters in the academic and industrial worlds who continue to provide valuable feedback and support for the ongoing development of this product.

Chris Dewhurst
Vancouver, B.C., Canada
June 1993

LogicWorks

1

Introduction

LogicWorks Features

Welcome to the world of electronics design. The purpose of this manual is to get you acquainted as quickly as possible with all the powerful editing and simulation features of LogicWorks.

LogicWorks provides full schematic editing features integrated with an interactive digital simulator.

General Features

Fully interactive operation. Any circuit, input, or device parameter change immediately affects displayed circuit activity. The timing diagram is updated and scrolls continuously as the simulation progresses.

Schematic Drawing Features

The DevEditor module (included with LogicWorks) allows any circuit to be assigned to a symbol, which can be created using the built-in drawing tools or imported from any external drawing program. Libraries of user-defined symbols are accessible from LogicWorks.

A circuit schematic can be up to a total of 5 feet by 5 feet. Any number of circuit windows can be open simultaneously, allowing easy copying of partial or complete diagrams from one file to another. Each circuit is displayed in a separate window with independent control of scroll and zoom.

Commands and drawing modes can be selected using menu items, keyboard equivalents, or a tool palette which is always visible in each window.

Any group of objects on the drawing can be repositioned with a simple click-and-drag mouse action. Signal lines are rerouted interactively to maintain right-angle connections.

Multiple signal-line routing methods allow most pin-to-pin connections to be made with only two mouse clicks.

Signal names are global across a schematic. Like-named signal traces on a page are thus logically connected for simulation and netlisting purposes.

Arbitrary user-defined text attributes can be attached to any device or signal in a circuit. This information can be used to generate SPICE-type netlists.

Circuit and timing diagrams can be printed.

Simulation Features

Full digital simulation capability. Circuit output may be displayed in the form of timing diagrams or on simulated output devices. Uses 13 signal states, including forcing and resistive drive levels to correctly simulate circuits with design errors such as unconnected inputs or conflicting outputs.

Device delay time for individual primitive components may be set to any integer from 0 to 32,767.

The timing display has adjustable time per division and reference-line placement.

Complex input sequences may be drawn directly on the timing diagram using the integrated waveform editor. Numerous timing editing features are available, including:

- Easy drawing and repositioning of signal edges
- Entry of Don't Know, HighZ, and Conflict states
- Cut/Copy/Paste/Duplicate of any grouping of signal traces
- An absolute time scale shows across the top of the timing diagram
- Delta-T measurements can be made by simply clicking the mouse

Common SSI and some MSI devices are implemented as primitives with hard-coded simulation functions. These can be used to create higher-level device functions.

Test and control devices such as switches and displays are active right on the schematic diagram, allowing circuit operation to be directly controlled and observed.

A Clock Generator device produces signals with variable period and duty cycle. Any number of clock generators can exist in one circuit.

Programmable Logic Arrays can be created with up to 96 inputs and 128 outputs with user-specified binary logic. Programmable Read Only Memories with up to 12 inputs and 128 outputs can also be simulated.

Save State/Restore State commands allow the user to reset the simulation to any saved state to retry after a circuit change. The simulation can be single-stepped or walked (2 time steps per second) using the tool palette.

RAM devices of any configuration from 1×1 to $1 \text{ mB} \times 64$ can be created and simulated (based on available memory). Device options include 0 or 1 OE inputs, 0 to 3 CE inputs, separate or combined data I/O pins, and three-state or normal outputs.

A **"strip chart" printing mode** allows continuous timing charts to be printed as the simulation progresses.

Interface Features

The Report Generator will generate the following types of text reports:

- A simple netlist format that lists all the device pins attached to each signal line

- Component listing, giving the name and type of each component

- Materials listing, showing all component types used and quantities

- Berkeley SPICE-type netlist, using node numbers

- Commercial SPICE format, using alphanumeric signal names

Limitations in This Version

The absolute maximum number of devices (including hidden devices in macros) is 32,767.

The typical number of devices without severe performance degradation ranges from 500   3,000, depending on your processor type and speed.

The maximum length of a pin number is four characters.

The maximum number of characters in an attribute block is 32,000.

The maximum number of pins on a device is 1,000.

The the entire circuit must fit into available memory.

Organization of This Manual

The LogicWorks manual is divided into the following chapters:

Chapter 1 **Introduction** An overview of the powerful editing and simulation features of LogicWorks.

Chapter 2 **Getting Started** Covers installation and initial startup.

Chapter 3 **Tutorial** Four exercises designed to introduce you to LogicWorks features.

Chapter 4 **User Interface** Provides detailed information on the use of windows, menus, keyboard commands, and other user controls and displays.

Chapter 5 **Creating the Schematic** Discusses the structure of a circuit diagram and how to create one from scratch.

Chapter 6 **Signals** Provides information on creating and editing signal lines as well as global and local names.

Chapter 7 **Devices** Discusses primitive and macro devices, placing and editing symbols on the schematic, and setting simulation characteristics of devices.

Chapter 8 **Simulation** Details the signal states, time units, and other aspects of the simulation. The timing diagram and waveform editing are also discussed.

Chapter 9 **PROM and PLA Devices** Discusses the creation and simulation of PROM and PLA devices.

Chapter 10 **Primitive Devices** Provides information on the simulation characteristics of the primitive device types and the creation and simulation of RAM devices.

Chapter 11 **Menu Reference** Provides specific information on the operation of each menu command.

Chapter 12 **The Device Editor** An in-depth look at the DevEditor module, the drawing environment used to create device symbols or general graphics used in LogicWorks schematics.

Chapter 13   Creating Text Reports   Discusses the Report Generator and the various commands used to create text files for documenting the current circuit.

Chapter 14   The Parts Window   Manipulation of device libraries.

The Appendixs contains information on file formats, error detection, keyboard shortcuts, and a glossary.

Notes Regarding Copyright

The LogicWorks software and manual are copyrighted products. The software license you have purchased entitles you to use the software on a single machine, with copies being made only for backup purposes. Any unauthorized copying of the program or documentation is subject to prosecution.

Note Regarding Trademarks

A number of product trademarks are referred to in this manual. Full credit for these is given on the copyright page.

2

Getting Started

This section gives you information on installing and starting up LogicWorks.

NOTE: Since the LogicWorks package and DOS are constantly being upgraded, there may be recent changes and additional information supplied in the file README.TXT, included with the package. It is important that you review this file prior to installation, since it may contain information that supersedes that given here.

We will be assuming that you are already familiar with general DOS operations. If you are not, work through the introductory sections of the DOS user's guide.

IMPORTANT: Before proceeding, make a backup copy and a working copy of your LogicWorks disks, then put the originals away for safekeeping.

Installation

The installation procedure depends on your disk storage configuration. LogicWorks requires a hard disk.

General Rules

LogicWorks requires that a number of files remain in the same directory as the main program. For this reason we suggest that you create a directory specifically for LogicWorks. The circuit and library files, however, can be located anywhere. The LogicWorks installation will place all files into this directory, along with the demo circuits and generic libraries. If you choose to move the libraries directory, you will need to change the LWSETUP.TXT file. See below for more information on how to do this.

Memory Requirements

LogicWorks requires at least 2 megabytes (mB) of extended memory to run. This generally requires a system with 4 mB of extended memory installed. If more memory is installed, that memory will be used to allow larger circuits and more circuits open at the same time.

Hard Disk Installation

Refer to the README.TXT file on the program disk for installation instructions. These will vary with different disk systems.

The Setup File

The Setup file is a text file that specifies some initial actions LogicWorks will take each time it is started up. The Setup file specifies the following information:

- Which libraries to open when the program is started

- Drawing characteristics

- Simulation characteristics

- Other options

The Setup file can be created or edited using your favorite programming editor or word processor. If you use a word processor, be sure to save the file using a "text only" option. The Setup file must be called "LWSETUP.TXT" and must be in the same folder as the LogicWorks program itself.

A typical Setup file looks like the following:

```
FOLDER LIBS;
{ The following libraries will be in directory "Libs" }
LIBRARY Generic.CLF;
LIBRARY 7400Devs.CLF;
LIBRARY IO.CLF;
LIBRARY Gates.CLF;
LIBRARY DemoLib.CLF;
```

The first word on each statement is a keyword which specifies a setup option. Statements are terminated by a semicolon and can contain embedded comments in braces. The most commonly used setup items are:

- FOLDER specifies the directory to look in for the following LIBRARY statements.

- LIBRARY specifies a library to open when the program is started.

For more information on the meaning and format of these statements, see "Setup File Format" in the Appendix.

The Graphical User Interface

Menus

The Main Menu will appear by holding down the right mouse button.

With the button held down, you can scroll through the menu commands by moving the mouse up and down over the menu. If you drag the mouse to the right over an arrow, a submenu will appear for that menu item.

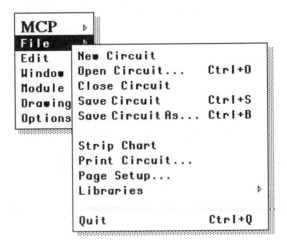

Drag the cursor over the item you wish to select and release the button. That operation will now be performed. There are Control-key equivalents for some commands. These are shown to the right of a command. These can be used from the keyboard at any time that the corresponding command is a valid action.

Windows

This is a typical window and its parts:

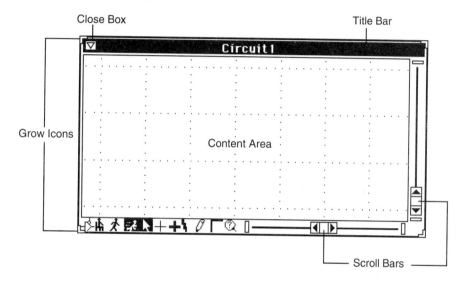

The window is made up of the content area, the title bar, and various icons. The grow icons allow you to make the window larger or smaller. The scroll bars let you scroll through the content area. The Close box will remove the window from the screen, possibly destroying the associated content.

Dialog Boxes

Various commands require user input in order to function. Dialog boxes are used for this purpose, allowing text to be entered, buttons to be pressed, and files to be found on your disks. The following Open dialog box is reached through selecting the Open Circuit command from the File menu.

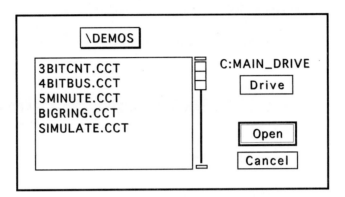

Use the mouse to locate the desired file. Click on Drive to cycle through the available drives on the system, one at a time. The Directory block shows the current directory (\DEMOS in the example above). Click on the block to move up in the directory structure. The file list box shows directories and the valid files in the current directory. Click on the desired directory or file to select it and then click on the Open button to enter that directory or open that file.

Other dialog boxes will have text items, buttons, checkboxes, and lists as well for input.

3

Tutorial

This tutorial section is divided into four main parts, allowing you to review the basic functions first, then learn about more-advanced features. The first tutorial, "The Five-Minute Schematic and Simulation," will give you a taste of how quickly you can put together a circuit with full simulation. The later sections are divided by subject, so you can study the features that are important for your application in more detail.

These tutorials are intended only to introduce you to LogicWorks features. For complete details on any subject, see the reference sections of this manual.

Tutorial Conventions

Mouse Terminology

Three different mouse button actions are used for various functions in LogicWorks:

Click   Press and release the left button without moving the mouse.
                     Example: To select a device, click on it.

Click and drag   Press the left button and hold it down while moving the mouse to the appropriate position for the next action.
                     Example: To move a device, click on it and drag it to the desired new position.

Double-click   Press and release the left button twice in quick succession without moving the mouse.
                     Example: To select an interconnected circuit group, double-click on any device in the group.

Step-by-Step Format

In the following tutorial sections, text preceded by this symbol ▶ is providing step-by-step instructions to achieve a specific goal. Other text presents background information and explanation of the actions being taken.

The Five-Minute Schematic and Simulation

This section will show you how quickly you can create and test a circuit using LogicWorks.

Starting LogicWorks

▶ Change to the new \LOGICWRK directory. Type logic and hit ⌐Enter⌐.

```
B:\>dir
 Volume in drive B is LOGICWORKS
 Directory of B:\

INSTALL  EXE    916105 07-18-91   1:00
TUNE     EXE     35211 10-01-91   9:05
README            100 07-18-91   1:09
         3 file(s)     951416 bytes
                       505344 bytes free


B:\>C:
C:\>cd \LOGICWRK
C:\LOGICWRK>
C:\LOGICWRK>logic
```

Several other directories are present inside the \LOGICWRK directory:

▓ \DEMOS contains a number of sample circuit files that will be referred to in this demo manual.

▓ \LIBS contains a basic set of device symbol libraries required for the demonstration. Many more libraries are included with the full package.

Once the program has started, you will be looking at a screen like this.

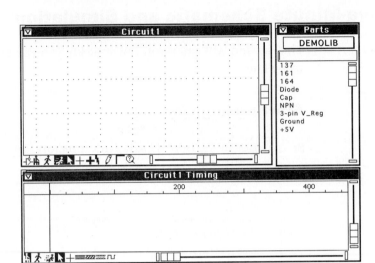

The circuit window is your viewport onto the circuit diagram; you will use the mouse to manipulate it. The timing window will display a timing diagram of the signals in your circuit. The parts window allows access to device libraries.

If you are using LogicWorks for schematic capture only, there is a Setup file option to hide the timing window by default.

Placing a Device

▶   Double-click on the device type "164" from the DemoLib library.

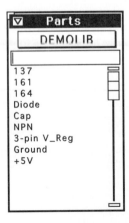

The cursor on the screen is replaced by a flickering image of the selected device type, in this case an 8-bit shift register.

The numbered devices in this library are generic 7400-series types. The labeling and simulation characteristics can be adjusted to match the various 7400 families on the market.

The list of open libraries can be changed manually using the Open Lib and Close Lib commands from the Libraries menu, or any collection of libraries can be opened automatically at startup by modifying the Setup file.

▶ Position this image somewhere near the center of the circuit window and click the mouse button. A permanent image of the device will now stay behind in that location, and the flickering image will continue to follow your movements.

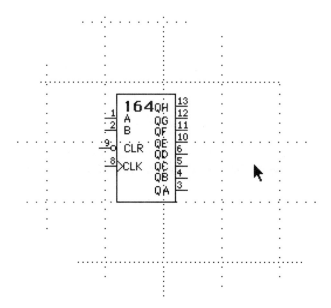

More devices of the same type could be created at this time, but in this case, select another device type.

▶ Press [Spacebar] to return to point mode. Notice that you can click and drag the device you placed to any desired new position.

▶ Click on the title block showing DEMOLIB and choose the GATES item. Double-click on the XNOR-2 type from the Gates library. The cursor will immediately change to match the new device type.

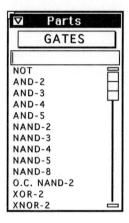

The devices in the Gates, Generic, and I/O libraries are called "primitive" types because they have built-in simulation models in LogicWorks. Other devices, such as those in the DemoLib library, are called "macro" types because their simulation models are made up of primitives. If LogicWorks is being used only for schematic entry, it is also possible to make symbols with no simulation function.

▶ Place one of these Exclusive-NOR gates adjacent to the 164 device so that the pins just touch, as shown.

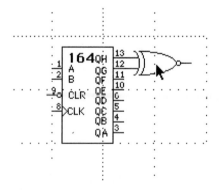

Whenever you place devices or signal lines so that they touch, you will notice that the signal lines flash briefly. This indicates that a logical connection has been made. You do not need to explicitly request a connection.

Moving a Device

▶ Point at the Exclusive-NOR gate and click and drag to the right. While you hold the mouse button you can drag the device to any desired new position. Note that any signal lines attached to the device are adjusted continuously to maintain connection.

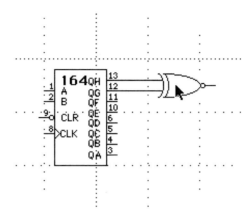

▶ Position the gate, as shown, to the right of the 164 device.

Drawing Signal Connections

▶ Attach a connection to the output of the gate by positioning the pointer near the endpoint of the pin and dragging away to the upper left.

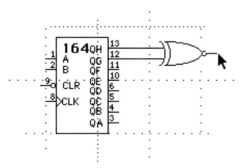

▶ Notice that two lines at right angles will follow your mouse movements to connect the starting and ending points.

▶ While moving the mouse, try pressing Alt and/or Ctrl and note the different line-routing methods available.

▶ Leave a right-angle line attached to the gate, as shown.

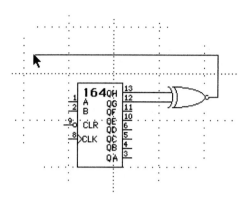

▶ Extend this line to connect to the B input of the 164 by clicking at the line endpoint where you left off, dragging the line to the B input, and releasing the mouse button.

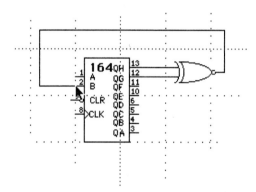

▶ Add a connection to pin A by clicking at the end of the pin, dragging the line down until it touches the signal line attached to B, then releasing the mouse button.

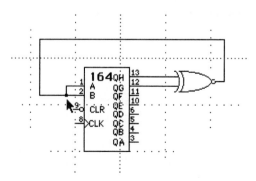

Notice that an intersection dot appears automatically whenever three or more lines intersect.

▶ Try repositioning a line segment by clicking and dragging anywhere along the length of the segment except at a corner or intersection.

Binary Switch Input Device

▶ Select the I/O library in the parts window and select the Switch device.

▶ Place it as shown on the diagram.

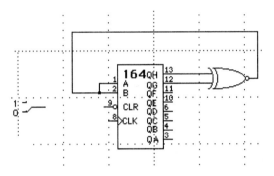

▶ Press ⌜Spacebar⌝ to return to point mode.

▶ Try clicking on the switch. Notice that it changes between the "0" and "1" states.

In order to move a switch, you must first select it by holding down ⌜⇧ Shift⌝ while clicking on it. This is necessary because the switch has a special response to a normal mouse click.

The devices in the I/O library can be used to actively control and observe the simulation right on the schematic. Each of these devices responds immediately to changes in the simulation in progress. The Hex Keyboard device is similar to the Switch device except that it operates on four lines at once.

Clock Generator Device

▶ Select a Clock Osc device from the Generic library and place it on the diagram, just below the switch.

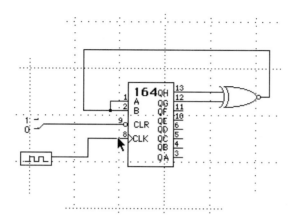

▶ Press ⌈Spacebar⌋ to return to point mode.

▶ Route wires from the switch and clock to the 164, as shown. Remember to try using ⌈Alt⌋ and ⌈Ctrl⌋ to route the wires.

While you have been working on the diagram, the LogicWorks simulator has been running continuously, simulating the effects of the new connections that are being made. So far, though, we have not asked it to display any results. This is done by either placing probes on the diagram or by displaying signals in the timing diagram.

Naming a Signal

▶ Click on the pencil icon in the tool palette at the lower-left corner of the circuit window to activate the name mode. The cursor will then change to a matching shape.

▶ Position the tip of the pencil anywhere along the length of the line running from the Clock Osc device and *press and hold* the mouse button. The cursor will change to an I-beam shape.

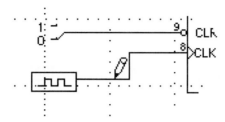

▶ Still holding down the mouse button, move the cursor to below the signal line.

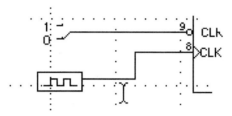

▶ Release the mouse button. A blinking insertion marker will appear.

▶ Type the name CLK on the keyboard, then press ⎗Enter or click the mouse button once.

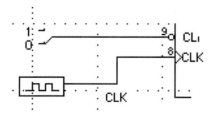

▶ Return to point mode and note that the name can be dragged to any desired position.

The Timing Diagram

You will immediately see the timing diagram come to life with the displayed values on the CLK line. Any named signal is shown by default in the timing diagram, although this can be disabled by using the Set Params command while the signal is selected.

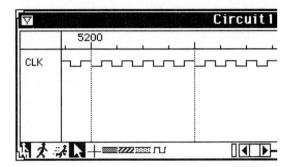

Reference lines are placed by default every 100 time units. You will see how to adjust this below. The time scale across the top shows the number of time units elapsed since the simulation was started.

▶ Again using the pencil cursor, name the two data lines from the shift register and the output line from the gate, as shown. The simulated output from these lines will immediately appear in the timing diagram.

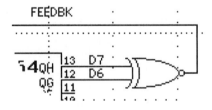

Timing Diagram Options

▶ Press ⌈Spacebar⌋ to return to point mode, then click on the signal CLK. It will become highlighted to indicate that it is selected.

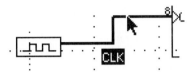

▶ Select the Timing Options command from the Options menu. This command lets you adjust how data is displayed in the timing window.

▶ Click on the Decrease button to decrease the display resolution (that is, display more timing data on the screen).

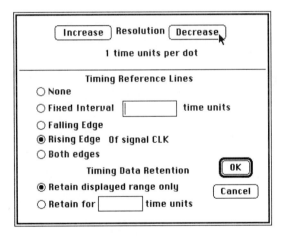

Display resolution can be adjusted from 4 screen dots per time unit to 100 time units per screen dot. The interpretation of a time unit is arbitrary, but it is convenient to think of them as nanoseconds.

▶ Click on the "Rising edge of signal CLK" button to place a reference line on the selected signal trace.

Probe Device

▶ Select the Probe type from the I/O library from the parts window.

▶ Place probes so that the pin contacts a signal line to view the simulation value on that line

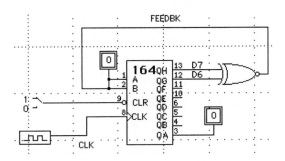

As the simulation progresses, the values on all probes are updated immediately. A similar device, the Hex Display, is also available to show groups of lines in hexadecimal. These simulation devices can be flagged to indicate that they are not a real part of the finished product and should not be included in any netlists or bills of materials.

Repositioning the Entire Circuit

▶ Double-click on any device in the circuit. This will highlight all devices and signals connected to that device.

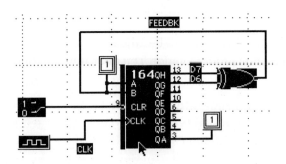

▶ Click and drag in any device in the circuit. Notice that an outline of the entire circuit follows your mouse movements. The circuit will be repositioned as soon as you release the mouse button.

Any group of selected items can be moved by this method. If the selected objects are attached to objects that aren't selected, all attaching lines will be adjusted at right angles to maintain a neat connectivity.

Setting Device Parameters

▶ Click in the window, but away from any circuit objects; this deselects everything.

▶ Click on the XNOR gate to select it.

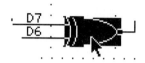

▶ Select the Set Params command from the Options menu.

▶ Click on the Increase button a couple of times to increase the propagation delay in this device.

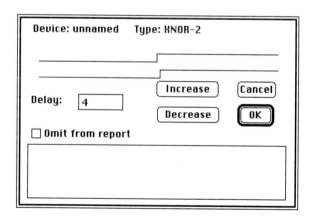

The Set Params command is used to view and set a variety of parameters associated with different object types. Any text typed into the Attributes box will be saved with the device and can be used to store special part numbers, simulation parameters, PCB layout parameters, and other data. More details on attributes are provided in a later section of this manual.

▶ Click on the OK button.

Device Delay on the Timing Diagram

Notice that the altered device delay immediately affects the simulation. You will see an increased delay between the clock reference lines and the changes in the FEEDBK signal.

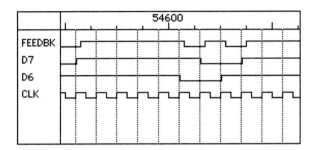

Interacting with the Simulation

▶ Try clicking on the switch hooked to the CLR input. Notice that it changes state and immediately affects the displayed simulation results.

▶ Try clicking on the simulation controls at the lower-left corner of the circuit or timing window.

▶ Clicking repeatedly on the Pause (sitting) icon causes the simulation to be single-stepped, allowing close inspection of circuit operation.

Saving the Circuit File

▶ Select the Save Circuit As command from the File menu and save your circuit so you can continue with it later

```
New Circuit
Open Circuit...     Ctrl+O
Close Circuit
Save Circuit        Ctrl+S
Save Circuit As... Ctrl+B
```

This ends the Five-Minute Schematic and Simulation tutorial section.

Schematic Editing

The object of this section of the tutorial is to take a closer look at the schematic editing features of LogicWorks. We will do this by making a number of modifications to the circuit file created in the five-minute demonstration.

Topics covered in this section include:

- Deleting and moving objects
- Selecting device types by name
- Device symbol rotation
- Using power and ground connectors
- Connecting signals by name
- Using Copy and Paste on circuit objects
- Naming devices
- Adding pin numbers to devices
- Placing text notations on the diagram

Opening a Circuit File

▶ Open the file you created in the first tutorial using the Open Circuit command from the File menu.

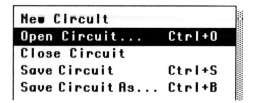

The file created in the first section is also supplied in the \DEMOS directory.

Deleting Objects

▶ Select the Zap (lightning bolt) tool in the tool palette. The cursor will change to match this icon.

This cursor is used to remove a single object from the diagram. When aimed at a device, the device is removed. When aimed at a signal line, the line segment is removed to the nearest device pin or intersection.

Breaking a Signal Line

▶ Zap the segment shown.

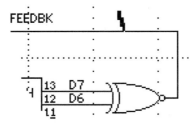

The signal has now been broken into two pieces and the signal name FEEDBK will become associated with the closest piece. You can click on the name to see which part highlights.

If the simulation is running, notice that the signal values are updated to reflect the unknown input values on the shift register.

Rotating a Device

▶ Before placing the next device, try pressing the arrow keys on the keyboard. Notice that this changes the orientation of the device symbol that is moving on the screen. Alternately you can click directly on the device icon in the tool palette to change its orientation.

There are actually eight different orientations available: the four major compass points, plus these directions with an additional flip around the major axis. The device icon in the tool palette shows the current selected orientation. This orientation also applies when groups of objects are pasted or duplicated.

Objects cannot be rotated after they are placed on the diagram.

Placing a Device

▶ Place an open-collector buffer on the diagram as shown.

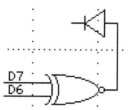

The open-collector buffer is a device that converts a low/high input into a low/high-impedance output. We will demonstrate how this works in conjunction with a pullup resistor in the following sections.

Resistor Device

▶ Select a Resistor device from the Generic library and place it as shown.

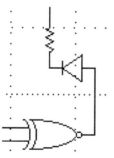

The Resistor device has special properties in the digital simulation. It conducts signal values in both directions but its output has a lower drive level than its input. Thus, it can be used as a pullup or pulldown resistor in circuit logic, or as a series resistor to simulate low-drive-level devices.

Power and Ground Connectors

▶ Select a +5V device from the DemoLib library and place it.

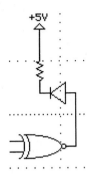

The +5V symbol is called a Signal Connector device and performs several functions. It puts out a constant high level for use in the simulation, it assigns the name "+5V" to the attached signal line, and it creates a logical connection to all other signal lines having the same symbol attached. You can create your own Signal Connectors for commonly used signals using the DevEditor module.

Clearing the Simulation

▶ Press (Spacebar) to return to the normal pointer, then wire these devices together as shown.

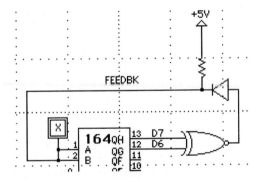

The timing diagram and probes will now be showing unknown values due to the broken connections and feedback in the circuit. This can be cleared using the Clear Unknowns command from the Options menu, or by clicking on the clear switch on the diagram.

Dragging Groups of Devices

▶ Select the three symbols shown by clicking on them while holding down ⌥Shift. Drag them to a more centered position, as shown.

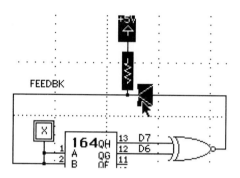

Connecting Signals by Name

▶ Select a NOT (Inverter) from the Gates library and place it as shown.

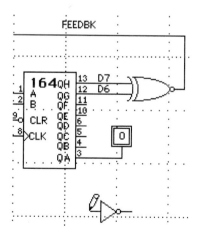

▶ Select the name mode (pencil) cursor and name this input D7, as described in the first tutorial. Note that the first character of the name will appear where the mouse button is *released*. Be careful to click the pencil at the *end* of the pin. Clicking in the middle of the pin will create a pin number.

When you place the label D7, you will notice that this line and the other D7 line will flash, indicating that a logical connection has been made. For simulation and netlisting purposes, these two signals are now connected together. Any like-named signals on the same page are considered to be connected.

▶ Double-click on either of the D7 signals to check connectivity.

▶ Label the output of the inverter NOTD7 and observe the inverted signal in the timing diagram.

Using Copy and Paste

To copy a section of the circuit to a new circuit file, do the following:

▶ Select the group of circuitry to be copied by clicking and dragging across a group of objects. Any object that intersects the rectangle will be selected.

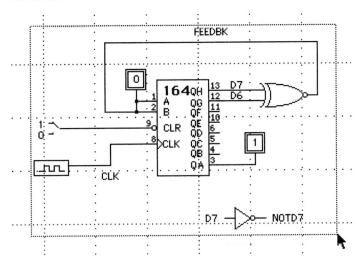

▶ Select the Copy command from the Edit menu.

▶ Select the New Circuit command from the File menu.

▶ Select the Paste command from the Edit menu.

A flickering outline of the entire circuit will follow your mouse movements. You can now place this group of objects anywhere on the new sheet. You can also use the arrow keys to reorient the circuit group before placing it.

The Cut, Copy, Paste, and Duplicate commands can be used on any single object or any group of selected objects.

▶ Close the new circuit (save it only if you want to) and return to the original circuit.

Naming Devices

Devices are named in a manner similar to signals. To name the devices U1, U2, and U3, follow these steps:

▶ Select the pencil cursor in the tool palette.

▶ Click the mouse button on the device symbol and hold it down while you drag to the desired position for the name.

▶ Release the mouse button.

▶ Type the desired name.

▶ Press ⌈←Enter⌋ or click the mouse button once.

▶ Repeat to name the devices as shown.

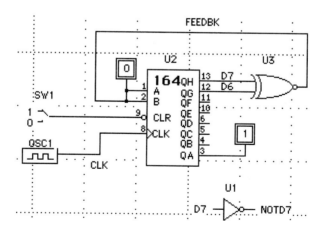

After they have been placed, device or signal names can be moved by dragging with the pointer. They can also be edited by clicking in an existing name with the pencil cursor.

Besides their use as labels on the schematic, device names are also used in a component list or bill of materials.

Pin Numbering

▶ Select the pencil cursor again and click it on a signal line very close to a device symbol, as shown. A blinking insertion marker will immediately appear next to the device.

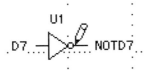

▶ Type up to four digits or letters for the pin number, then press ⏎Enter or click the mouse button once.

Pin numbers can only be positioned directly on device pins and cannot be moved. Pin numbers are used to distinguish device pins when a netlist is created. Most non-gate library devices have pin numbers already defined for the most common package type. The default pin numbers can be specified in the device library, or they can be edited right on the diagram.

Placing Text on the Diagram

The pencil cursor can also be used to place random text notations anywhere on the diagram.

▶ Click on the diagram, not near any device or signal line, and a blinking insertion marker will appear at that point.

▶ Type any desired text, using ⏎Enter to create multiple lines.

▶ Click the mouse button once to complete the text item.

▶ Return to point mode, then click on the text item you just typed to select it.

▶ Choose the Set Params command from the Options menu. The dialog box that appears allows you to pick from several framing options and set the text size for the selected item.

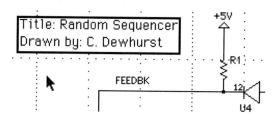

▶ Save the file you have created to this point for use later on.

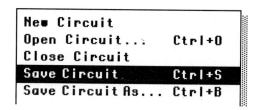

This ends the tutorial section on general schematic editing.

Digital Simulation

This section of the tutorial will provide you with a closer look at the integrated digital simulator in LogicWorks, including discussion of the following topics:

- Types of devices simulated

- Controlling the simulation

- Representation of time and signal values

- Using the waveform editor

Logic States

▶ Create the circuit below using the O.C. Buf-1 and Probe devices.

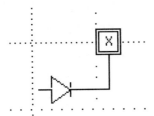

LogicWorks uses a total of 13 different logic values for signals in order to handle different drive levels and unknown situations. The probe will display an X for any of the six possible "Don't Know" states. In this case, the X results from the fact that the device input is unconnected.

▶ Add a Switch device to the input of the buffer, as shown.

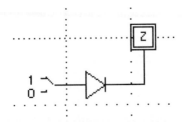

▶ Click on the switch a couple of times and note that the buffer output alternates between the "0" and Z states.

The Z value indicates an undriven line. Multiple open-collector or three-state devices can drive a line to simulate bus or wired-AND logic.

Circuits with Feedback

▶ Click on the Buffer device and use the Duplicate command to create another one as shown.

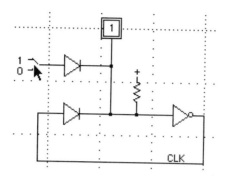

▶ Add a pullup resistor (Pullup B in the Generic library) and an inverter (NOT in the Gates library), and wire them as shown.

▶ Click on the switch and notice the oscillation that occurs due to the feedback in this circuit.

▶ Name the output signal CLK so that it shows in the timing diagram.

Using the Signal Probe Tool

▶ Click on the signal probe tool in the tool palette.

▶ Click the tip of the probe tool along any signal line. It will show the current value of the signal as the simulation progresses.

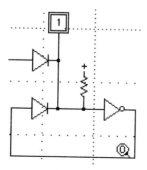

You can also use this tool to enter new signal values by typing 0 or 1 on the keyboard while the mouse button is pressed. Stuck-at, unknown, and high-impedance levels can also be inserted.

Time Values

LogicWorks uses integers to represent simulated time values. The interpretation of these numbers is left to the user, although it is usually convenient to think of them as nanoseconds.

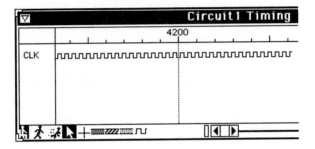

LogicWorks uses an *event driven* simulator, meaning that device values are recalculated only when an input change occurs. Thus, the speed at which the simulation progresses does not depend on delay or other time values in the circuit.

Primitive Devices

▶ Click on the Inverter device to select it, then select the Set Params command from the Options menu.

The inverter is classified as a *primitive* device because its simulation function is built into the program. Primitive devices have a single integer which defines the delay from any input pin to any output pin for any transition. More-complex models can be implemented by building macro devices out of the existing primitives.

▶ Click on the Delay box and change the value to 5 units, then click on the OK button. Notice the effect this delay change has on the period of the oscillation in this circuit.

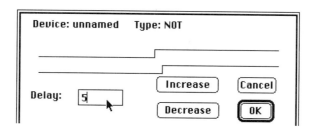

"0" and "1" Signals

▶ Select a 161 4-bit counter device from the DemoLib library and place it in the circuit as shown.

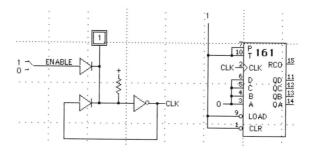

▶ Add the names 0, 1, CLK, and ENABLE using the pencil cursor, as previously described.

The signal names "0" and "1" indicate to the simulator that those lines should be permanently set to the corresponding logic levels.

Macro Devices

Add the names D0 to D3 using the following procedure:

▶ Name the least significant counter output D0 using the usual technique.

▶ Hold down Ctrl and Alt while you click on each higher pin in turn. This will automatically place sequential numbers on the lines clicked.

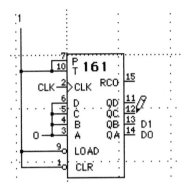

Notice that the traces D0 to D3 in the timing diagram will show unknown values because the counter has never been cleared to a known state.

▶ Select the Clear Unknowns command from the Options menu. This resets all storage elements to the "0" state and clears unknown lines.

▶ Click on the 161 device to select it, then select the Set Params command from the Options menu.

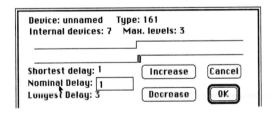

The 161 counter is a *macro device*, meaning that its logic function is implemented using a combination of the LogicWorks primitive devices. Because of this, the Set Params display is more complex, showing the shortest and longest delay paths that can be expected through this device.

▶ Click on the OK button in the Set Params box.

Controlling Simulation Speed

The Pause, Walk, and Run icons at the lower-left corner of the screen are used to control the simulation.

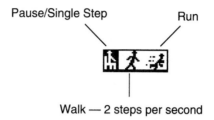

Pause/Single Step   Run

Walk — 2 steps per second

▶ Click on the Pause icon a number of times. Notice that each click causes the simulation to be advanced to the next time unit having any signal activity.

▶ Click on the Walk and Run icons, and notice their effect on simulation speed.

The timing window can be closed (by clicking on the Go-Away box at the upper-left corner) at any time without closing the circuit file. The simulation will actually advance more quickly with this window closed, since screen updating is not required.

Moving Timing Traces

▶ Click and drag the name CLK in the timing diagram vertically to reposition it relative to the other traces.

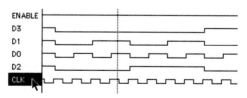

You can reposition any group of traces for ease in making timing comparisons. By holding down ⇧Shift while clicking on multiple trace names, any number of traces can be moved at once.

Drawing Timing Waveforms

▶ Click on the Pause icon to stop the simulation.

The editing tools in the timing window tool palette are disabled when the simulation is running.

▶ Use the Zap cursor to remove the Switch device from the circuit.

▶ Select the Clear Timing command from the Options menu. This removes all past and pending signal changes from memory.

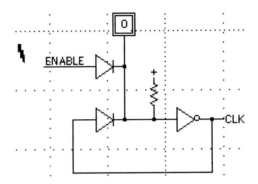

Because the switch has been removed, the ENABLE line is no longer being driven by any device. If the simulation were allowed to proceed at this time, the unknown value at this input would propagate through the circuit. If signal changes are drawn on the timing diagram, however, these values override the simulated values on that line.

▶ Click anywhere in the timing window to activate it.

The tool palette in the timing window contains tools to set up various signal values on timing traces. The time values indicate the time value of the current cursor position and the difference in time between the point where the cursor was pressed and its current position.

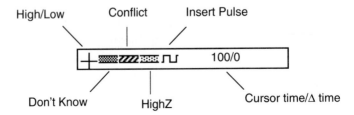

▶ Click on the high/low tool.

▶ Move the crosshair cursor to a position to the right of the ENABLE name on the timing diagram, then *press and hold* the mouse button.

▶ Move the mouse and notice that a vertical movement causes the line to take on high and low values, and a horizontal movement determines the time of the next event.

▶ Release the mouse button so that the signal is in the low state to time 50, as shown.

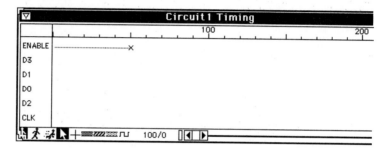

▶ Move the crosshair cursor to a position to the right of the signal line just drawn and press and hold the button again.

▶ Draw a line in the high state to time 100, as shown.

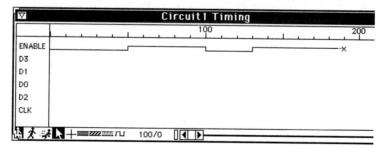

▶ Use the same technique to draw the remaining changes.

▶ Select the Save State command from the Options menu.

For cases in which timing data has been generated externally, text describing the signal changes can be used to paste timing information into the timing diagram.

▶ Click on the Walk icon to proceed though a slow simulation of the input sequence just drawn.

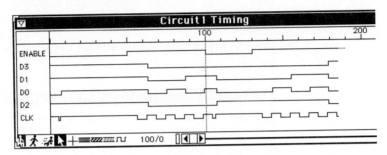

▶ Select the Restore State command from the Options menu. Note that this resets the simulation to the point it was at when the Save State command was issued.

This ends the simulation tutorial. Save the file if you wish, but it will not be used again in subsequent tutorials.

Report Generation

LogicWorks is capable of generating text netlists, parts lists, and files for SPICE-based analog simulators.

This section assumes that you have run through the previous tutorial sections and understand the basic techniques of placing and naming LogicWorks devices and signals.

Creating Analog Schematics

LogicWorks is well suited as a schematic entry mechanism for analog simulators, such as SPICE. If the digital simulator is not normally used, a Setup file option is available to disable the simulator and hide the timing window by default.

▶ Open the sample circuit file SPICE from the \DEMOS directory.

▶ Select the Show Circuit Info command from the Options menu.

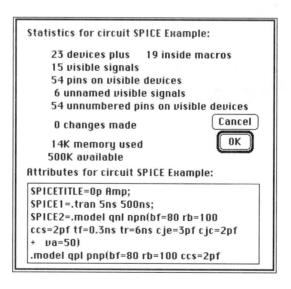

```
Statistics for circuit SPICE Example:

    23 deuices plus      19 inside macros
    15 uisible signals
    54 pins on uisible deuices
     6 unnamed uisible signals
    54 unnumbered pins on uisible deuices

     0 changes made                    [ Cancel ]

    14K memory used                    [  OK  ]
    500K available

Attributes for circuit SPICE Example:

SPICETITLE=Op Amp;
SPICE1=.tran 5ns 500ns;
SPICE2=.model qnl npn(bf=80 rb=100
ccs=2pf tf=0.3ns tr=6ns cje=3pf cjc=2pf
+  ua=50)
.model qpl pnp(bf=80 rb=100 ccs=2pf
```

In this example file, the circuit attributes block is being used to store SPICE parameters that are to appear at the beginning and end of each netlist file.

▶ Click on the OK button.

▶ Click on the Vin voltage source and select the Set Params command.

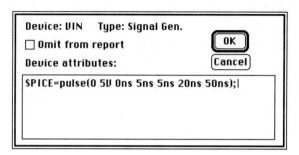

This device, and all others in the circuit, contains an attribute field called SPICE. The contents of this field will be inserted in the output file for each device. It can therefore be used to specify any required simulation parameters for the device.

Using this attribute feature, LogicWorks can produce a complete SPICE-format file that needs no modification for use in analog simulation.

LogicWorks comes complete with a library of devices specifically designed for use with SPICE. Symbols are provided for all the standard models. This library should be used for creating SPICE schematics because it ensures a pin definition order that matches SPICE requirements.

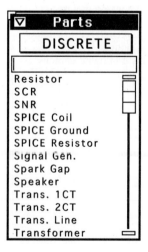

Creating a SPICE Netlist

▶ Select the Report command from the Module menu.

▶ Click on the SPICE Report Type option.

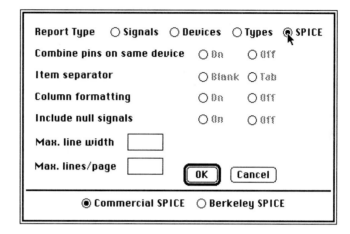

▶ Click on the Commercial or Berkeley option.

▶ Click on the OK button.

▶ Select a suitable name and location for the output text file.

Once the text file is created, it can be read directly into any SPICE package or opened using a word processor for further editing. See the detailed section later in this manual on creating files for SPICE.

This ends the Report Generation section of the tutorial.

4

User Interface

This chapter provides general information on the use of windows, drawing tools, and other user-interface features of LogicWorks.

Mouse Terminology

Three different mouse button actions are used for various functions in LogicWorks. For clarity we will use consistent terminology when referring to these actions in the remainder of the manual:

Click Press and release the left button without moving the mouse.
Example: To select a device, click on it.

Click and drag Press the left button and hold it down while moving the mouse to the appropriate position for the next action.
Example: To move a device, click on it and drag it to the desired new position.

Double-click Press and release the left button twice in quick succession without moving the mouse.
Example: To select an interconnected circuit group, double-click on any device in the group.

Dialog Boxes

Many LogicWorks functions require information from the user. To accomplish this, a special window called a *dialog box* is displayed, such as the following one which is displayed when a Set Params command is executed for a signal.

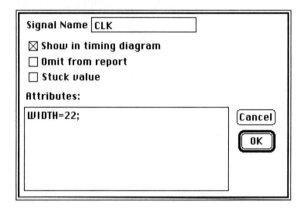

The dialog box consists of boxes and buttons that allow text to be entered or options to be set. Use the mouse to select the item you wish to alter. Either position the cursor in a text box and type, or click on a checkbox or radio button to alter the states described by that item. Click on OK when done, or Cancel to discard all changes.

LogicWorks Windows

LogicWorks uses two main types of windows, or screen areas:

Circuit Windows

Each circuit window displays one page of a circuit schematic. The title on a circuit window will be the name of the circuit file displayed in that window, as in "CPUBoard". Any number of circuits can be displayed simultaneously. At any given time only one circuit is "current," that being the one in the topmost window. Any other window can be made current simply by clicking the mouse anywhere in that window.

Timing Window

There is only one timing window, which shows the timing data for the current circuit. Editing operations possible in the timing window are explained in Chapter 8, Simulation.

Any of these windows can be resized or removed from the screen altogether if desired. In most cases, while you are working on a circuit schematic you will want to enlarge the circuit window to use the entire screen by clicking the menu button over the title bar and selecting the Full Size option.

Closing a Window

To remove the timing window from the screen, simply click the mouse button with the pointer positioned in the Go-Away box at the top-left corner of the window. Removing the timing window has no effect on your circuit or on the simulation in progress, except that the simulation will run faster without the need to scroll the timing diagram. The timing window can be redisplayed using the Window menu described in a later section.

Clicking in the Go-Away box in a circuit window has the effect of closing the circuit. This is the same as selecting Close from the File menu. If you have made any changes since the last Open or Save operation, you will be asked whether you want to save those changes in the file.

Redisplaying a Window

When a circuit window is closed, that circuit is closed and the window removed from the screen and the Window menu. To redisplay a circuit window that has been closed, you must use the Open command from the File menu to reread the file from your disk.

Resizing a Window

To enlarge or reduce either the circuit or timing windows, position the pointer in one of the grow icons at the corner of the window and press and hold the mouse button. As long as the button is held down, a gray outline of the window will track the mouse movements. When the button is released, the window will be redrawn with the new size and shape.

To expand a circuit or timing window to fill the whole screen, click the menu button on the mouse with the pointer over the title bar. A short menu will appear that allows you to enlarge or shrink the window. (You can also close the window from this menu.)

Moving a Window

To move either the circuit or timing windows, position the pointer in the title bar anywhere along the top edge of the window and press and hold the mouse button. As long as the button is held down, a gray outline of the window will track the mouse movements. When the button is released the window will be redrawn at its new position.

The Window Menu

The Window menu provides a means of displaying any window currently in use, as well as redisplaying the timing window. Simply select the window you would like to bring to the foreground from the list in the Window menu.

Using the Keyboard

The keyboard is absolutely required only when entering names for devices or signals, or for placing random text notations on the drawing. The ⸢Ctrl⸥, ⸢⇧Shift⸥, and ⸢Alt⸥ keys can be used with many editing operations to invoke special features such as auto-alignment, auto-naming, and different signal-line drawing methods. In addition, the arrow keys can be used as a convenient way of setting symbol rotation while placing devices or pasting circuit groups. These options are described in detail in the relevant chapters, but a short summary of special key usage is given in the Appendix.

Tool Palette and Status Display

Located at the bottom-left corner of each circuit window is the tool palette and status display shown below. The individual items in this display are described in the following sections.

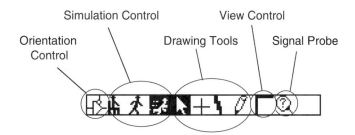

Orientation Control

The Orientation icon shows the direction of the next device or circuit scrap to be pasted into the schematic. The orientation can be changed by clicking on the icon, using the arrow keys on the keyboard, or by using the Orientation menu command. More information on device rotation and mirroring is given in Chapter 5, Creating the Schematic.

Simulation Control

The three simulation icons are used to pause, single-step, or walk (2 time steps per second) the simulation. More information is given in Chapter 8, Simulation.

Schematic Drawing Tools

The drawing tools are used to set the cursor mode for schematic editing. More information on cursor modes is given in the next section.

Cursor Modes

The small shape that tracks the mouse position on the screen is known as the pointer or cursor. In LogicWorks there are a number of different cursors that determine what action will be performed when the mouse button is clicked. Following is a summary of the cursor modes. Detailed descriptions of operations performed in each mode are provided in later sections on each type of object affected.

Normal or Point Mode

The pointer (arrow) cursor is used while selecting or dragging objects, extending signals, or activating input devices.

Signal-Drawing Mode

The crosshair cursor is used while creating a new signal line or extending an existing signal. Clicking once fixes a corner, double-clicking terminates the line. Note that most signal-drawing operations can also be done in point mode. To prevent inadvertent creation of signal segments, the Ctrl key must be held to draw a freestanding signal, not starting from a device.

Zap Mode ⚡

The lightning bolt cursor is used to remove single objects. Position the tip of the lightning bolt on an object you wish to delete, then click to remove it.

NOTE: This cannot be undone!

Objects can also be removed in groups by selecting them and using the Clear command or ⌫Backspace.

Name Mode ✎

The pencil cursor is used to select a signal or device to name, or to place random text on the diagram. Point at the item you want to name and press and hold the mouse button. Move to where you want the name to appear, then release the button.

Text Mode I

The I-beam cursor appears after the pencil cursor while selecting a screen position for a name. Release the mouse button at the point where you want the name to begin.

Set Display Area Mode ⌐ ⌐

The right-angle cursors appear while selecting a screen area to be displayed using the Set Display Area command in the Drawing menu. Dragging down and right zooms in, dragging up and left zooms out. Hold down Ctrl to prevent return to point mode. Hold down Alt to zoom in to a maximum of 100%.

Signal Probe Mode 🔍

The signal probe cursor is used to view and change signal values on the schematic. Click on the signal to view with the tip of the probe, and the cursor displays changes in signal value. Type 0 or 1 on the keyboard to enter a value. For more information, see Chapter 8, Simulation.

5

Creating the Schematic

This chapter provides information on the elements of a LogicWorks circuit and how to create one.

Definition of a Circuit

In LogicWorks, the term *circuit* refers to a complete, independent logical entity. A single circuit is stored in a single file and no logical connections are made between circuits. Each circuit is drawn on the screen as if it were on a single piece of paper, although it may have to be broken up into a number of individual sheets of paper for printing or plotting.

Types of Objects in a Circuit

A LogicWorks circuit is made up of three types of entities: devices, signals, and text objects.

■ A device is an object comprising a symbol, signal connection points called "pins," and optional simulation information. A device in LogicWorks generally corresponds to a physical device in a circuit, although a number of "pseudo-devices," such as Page Connectors and power and ground symbols, are used for specific diagramming functions. For more information, see Chapter 7, Devices.

■ A signal is a conductive path between devices. Signal connections can be made visually by drawing lines between device pins, or logically by name. For more information, see Chapter 6, Signals.

■ A text object is used to place a title block or other notation on the diagram. Text can be typed and edited directly within LogicWorks. Text objects are not associated with any other object and are not accessible through net or component lists. The naming and attribute facilities should be used to associate text with specific devices or signals. Text operations are described later in this chapter.

Setting the Page Size

LogicWorks supports various printers for output on a variety of media. For this reason, there can be complex interactions between the drawing area allocated for each page and the way the schematic is presented when it is output on various kinds of devices.

In this manual the term *page* is used to refer to a circuit page, which is the single, contiguous area that is viewed in one circuit window. The term *sheet* is used to refer to the physical sheet of paper that the diagram is printed or plotted on.

Selecting and Placing Devices

Devices are placed on the diagram by selecting the device type by name in the parts window and double-clicking the mouse button in the desired position. Several alignment options can be invoked by pressing Ctrl or ⇧ Shift while positioning a device.

Operation of the Parts Window

The parts window allows access and manipulation of device libraries.

Placing a Device

After clicking on the part name in the parts window, a flickering image of the selected device will follow the mouse movements until you click the button again, causing a device to be created at that point. The image continues to follow your movements, allowing you to create multiple devices of the same type. You can return to the normal pointer by pressing [Spacebar] or selecting another menu command.

Auto-Alignment Options

While you are moving the flickering device image on the screen, several auto-alignment options are available using [⇧ Shift] and [Ctrl]:

- The [⇧ Shift] key is used to force vertical or horizontal alignment of successive devices placed on the diagram. It will have no effect while the first device is being placed after a library selection, but thereafter the flickering device image will be constrained to vertical or horizontal alignment with the first one.

- The [Ctrl] key is used to force equal spacing between subsequent devices. It will have no effect until two devices have been placed in succession after a library selection. After the second device is placed, it will place the flickering image at increments equal to the distance between the first and second devices.

Simply holding down these two keys as the first and subsequent devices are placed will ensure perfect alignment of a row of symbols.

Note that these alignment options also apply to placing entire groups of circuitry using the Paste or Duplicate commands.

Automatic Connection

If you place a device in such a way that any of its pins contact any other signal lines or pins, connections will be made automatically at those points. There are no explicit commands in LogicWorks to make or break connections between two lines. Connection marker dots are added automatically at any intersection of three or more lines belonging to the same signal.

Disabling Automatic Connection

Connection "hit testing" can be disabled by pressing [Alt] while clicking the mouse button. This allows the device to be selected again and moved without interactions with other objects in the circuit. For more information on this process, see the Paste command in Chapter 11, Menu Reference.

Opening and Closing Libraries

The list of libraries in the parts window is controlled by the Open Lib/Close Lib commands and by the Setup file (described in Chapter 2, Getting Started, and in the Appendix). Creating and maintaining your own device libraries is described in Chapter 12, The Device Editor.

Using the Duplicate and Copy/Paste Commands

An alternative method of placing a device is to select an existing device of the desired type (by clicking on it) and using the Duplicate command or the Copy and Paste commands.

Device Rotation and Mirroring

Device symbols can be placed in one of eight rotations/reflections, as shown in the following example:

	Standard	1st Rotation	2nd Rotation	3rd Rotation
Normal				
Mirrored				

Limitations on Device Rotation

Device rotation can be selected before or after the device type is selected from the parts window. Once a device is placed, it cannot be rotated.

Some symbols, especially those containing text, will not rotate correctly in some orientations. The underlying operating system in its current form does not support rotated text on the screen. LogicWorks attempts to reposition characters into a sensible order, but this may not be possible if the characters were entered separately, rather than as a string. Separate characters in a word or number may become inverted or may overlap.

If you need a specific device in an orientation that does not appear correctly when rotated automatically, you can copy the picture onto the clipboard (using Copy), modify it, and create a new copy of the device using the DevEditor module.

Setting Device Orientation

The current orientation is shown by the small device icon at the lower-left corner of the circuit window, as follows:

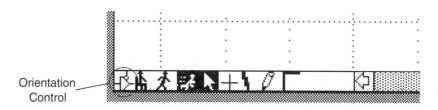

Orientation Control

The orientation can be changed either by clicking on this icon, by using the arrow keys on the keyboard, or by selecting the Orientation menu command. Multiple hits on a arrow key causes the orientation to flip between the two mirroring options, as follows:

Hit left-arrow key for

Hit it again for

Hit right-arrow key for

Hit it again for

Hit down-arrow key for

Hit it again for

Hit up-arrow key for

Hit it again for

The icon has sensitive areas that determine which orientation is selected, as follows:

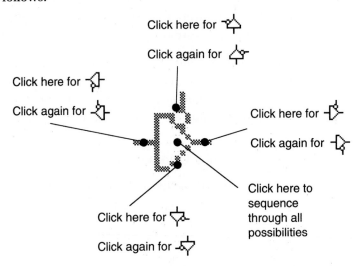

The Orientation menu command causes the orientation to sequence through all possibilities, equivalent to clicking in the center of the Orientation icon.

The rotations are relative to the image that is stored in the device library, which is assumed to be in "standard" position (facing right). That is, if an image is stored with a vertical orientation, such as:

then the first rotation (as indicated by a vertical icon) will be:

The current orientation also affects circuit scraps that are manipulated using the Paste or Duplicate commands. Again, the orientation is relative to the orientation of the devices in the source circuit.

Drawing Grid

All drawing takes place on invisible grid lines spaced every 5 screen dots at Normal Size. Device symbols and signal lines are automatically aligned with this grid, making it much easier to align objects on a diagram. The only items not affected by this grid are device and signal names and independent text items, which can be placed in any desired position.

A visible drawing grid is displayed in the circuit window spaced at every 10 invisible grid spaces. This grid is provided to assist with drawing and can be removed using the Display Options command from the Drawing menu.

Selecting Circuit Objects

Some of the menu commands—for example, Cut, Copy, Clear, Duplicate, and Set Params—operate on the currently selected items. The items selected will be highlighted to distinguish them on the screen. If no item is selected, these commands will be disabled.

LogicWorks allows you to select items by one of the following methods:

- Select a single device or text item by clicking the mouse button with the pointer positioned anywhere inside the item.

- Select a single signal by clicking anywhere along the signal line. This selects only the part of the signal directly attached to the clicked line. Double-clicking on the signal selects all parts of the signal in the circuit, including logical connections by name.

- Select any group of adjacent items by clicking and dragging across the group. A flickering rectangle will follow the mouse movement. Any object that intersects this rectangle when the button is released will be selected.

- Switches and keyboards can be selected only by holding down ⇧Shift while clicking. This is necessary because a normal click is used to change the state of these devices.

- Select a group of interconnected devices and signals by double-clicking on any device in the group. If a circuit is completely interconnected, this will select the entire circuit.

- The Select All command from the Edit menu selects all items in the circuit.

- The ⌈⇧Shift⌋ key can be used in combination with any of the above methods to select multiple items. When ⌈⇧Shift⌋ is pressed, the previously selected items are not deselected when a new item is clicked. You can thus add to the selected group until the desired collection of items is selected.

- Holding down ⌈Ctrl⌋ while clicking the pointer causes stacked objects to be selected in the opposite order from normal. This can be used, for example, to select a signal name that has accidently moved under a device, since devices take precedence over signal names.

Deselecting a Device or Signal

All currently selected devices or signals are deselected by pressing the mouse button with the pointer positioned in the circuit window, but not near any object. A single item can be deselected by holding down ⌈⇧Shift⌋ while you click on it.

Repositioning the Entire Circuit

An entire circuit can be repositioned on the page by using the Select All command from the Edit menu, then clicking on and dragging any device in the diagram. A flickering image of the entire drawing will then follow the mouse movements.

Placing Random Text on the Diagram

If you click the pencil cursor on the diagram away from any device or signal line, a blinking cursor will appear at that point, and you will be able to type any desired text on the diagram.

NOTE: Random text items are not associated with any particular device or signal on the screen and should not be used to name or set attributes for devices or signals. The text in these boxes is not accessible in net or component lists. Use the naming feature to attach names to devices and signals.

Editing Random Text

If you click the pencil cursor inside an existing text item, the insertion point will be positioned at the click point. You can then use normal text-editing techniques to modify the text.

Text boxes can be Zapped, Duplicated, Cut, Copied, Pasted, and dragged just like any other item on the screen. See the descriptions of these commands for more information.

Setting Text Box Appearance

The Set Params command can be used to modify the appearance of a selected text item. A dialog box will appear, allowing the selection of a border, optional ruling between the text lines, and text size, as follows:

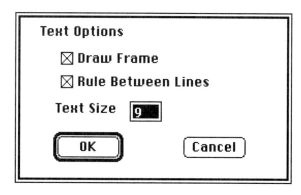

Text Dragging

To allow precision alignment of text objects relative to other items on the diagram, the grid alignment can be overridden while these objects are dragged. This is done by pressing Ctrl while performing the drag operation with *only* text objects selected.

6

Signals

This chapter provides information on drawing and interconnecting signals.

Drawing Signals

Signal lines are drawn in either point mode or signal-drawing mode.

Point Mode

The arrow cursor allows you to extend an existing signal line from an end point or intersection. If you start from the middle of a line, you will simply reposition the existing line, not extend it. Position the pointer with the tip at the end of an existing line (or at the end of a device pin), then press and hold the mouse button while you move in the desired direction. Note that the program creates two lines forming a right angle that follow the mouse movements. The direction of the first line depends on the direction of the line being extended. Alternate line-routing methods can be activated by pressing Alt and Ctrl, as follows:

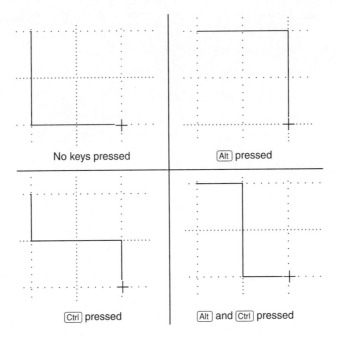

The Alt key inverts the order of line drawing, and the Ctrl key switches to three line segments with a center break. Also, ⇧Shift constrains the movement to a single vertical or horizontal line.

When you release the mouse button, the lines are made permanent. If the button is released while the pointer is on another signal line, a connection is made at that point.

Signal-Drawing Mode

Signal-drawing mode using the crosshair cursor is similar in operation to point mode except for the following:

- Drawing can start from anywhere along the length of a signal line, not just at the ends as in point mode.

- The mouse button can be released while drawing is in progress. The flickering lines do not become permanent until the button is pressed again.

- Line drawing continues until a connection is made to another signal, you double-click the mouse button, you hit Spacebar, or you click the button outside the current window.

- A signal line can be started from anywhere in the diagram (not just from an existing line) by holding down Ctrl while clicking the mouse button.

Editing Signal Lines

The following features are available to assist with editing signal lines:

- Zap mode (entered by selecting the Zap command from the Edit menu or the Zap icon in the tool palette) allows you to remove any single line segment from a signal connection. Zapping on a signal line removes only the selected line segment, up to the nearest intersection, device pin, segment join point, or to the edge of the window.

- Selecting a signal line (by clicking anywhere along its length) and hitting ←Backspace or selecting the Clear command removes an entire signal trace. *Be careful, because this cannot be undone!*

- Drawing backward along the length of an existing line causes the line to be shortened to the point where you release the button.

- Clicking and dragging a signal-line segment allows you to reposition the line. Vertical lines can be moved horizontally and vice versa.

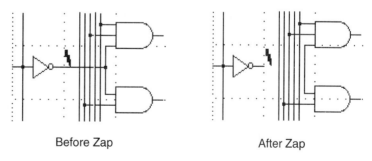

Before Zap   After Zap

Interconnecting Signals

If you draw a signal line so that the end of the line contacts a second signal line, then those two signals will be interconnected. Also, if you place a new device so that one of its pins contacts an existing signal line, that pin will be connected to the signal. If both of the two signals being connected were named, you will be prompted to choose the name of the resulting signal. Whenever three or more line segments belonging to the same signal meet at a given point, an intersection dot will be placed at that point automatically.

Connecting Signals by Name

Signal names can be used to make logical connections between wires that are not visually connected on the schematic. The following rules apply:

- Signal names are known throughout the circuit. Like-named signal traces are thus logically connected for simulation and netlisting purposes.

- Whenever a signal name is added or changed, the circuit is checked for a change in connectivity. If the name is now the same as another signal in this circuit, the two signals are merged into one. Whenever a name change causes two signals to be connected, both parts will flash on the screen to confirm the connection.

- If a signal segment was previously connected by name to others and the name is changed, the logical connection is broken.

Power and Ground Connections

LogicWorks uses a pseudo-device symbol called a Signal Connector device to maintain connectivity between like-named power and ground symbols that are used on circuit diagrams.

As soon as a ground symbol is placed on the diagram, the attached signal is named "Ground" (the name is invisible). This causes it to be connected by name to any other grounded signals or signals explicitly named "Ground".

Connectivity can be checked at any time by double-clicking on any ground or power line. This will highlight all other like-named lines on the diagram.

Note that this feature is not limited to power and ground lines, but can be used anywhere it is desired to use a special symbol to connect common signals.

Using Signal Connector Devices

Signal Connector devices are placed on the diagram just like any other LogicWorks device. A set of standard power-supply symbols are included with LogicWorks in the Connect library. If you join two different Signal Connector devices, you will be prompted to provide a name for the resulting signal.

Creating Signal Connectors in a Library

Signal Connector devices (like Page Connectors) are special primitive pseudo-devices in LogicWorks and can be created using the Set Primitive Type command in the DevEditor module to select the SIGCONN primitive type. For more-detailed information on this procedure, see Chapter 12, The Device Editor.

NOTE: The signal attached to a Signal Connector device is actually named to match the *pin name* of the signal connector pin specified in DevEditor, *not* the type name. In most of the power and ground symbols provided with LogicWorks, these two names are the same. It is possible, however, to create a symbol called, for example, "Ground" in the library which actually names the attached signal "GND". The ground symbol in the SPICE Devices library is an example of this in that it names the attached signal "0" to match the SPICE ground-naming convention.

Checking Signal Interconnection

Double-clicking anywhere along a signal line will cause that signal segment and all logically connected segments to be selected.

Setting Signal Parameters

Selecting a signal and selecting the Set Params command will display the following dialog box:

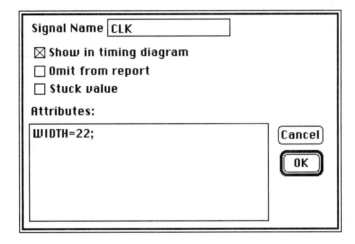

Show in Timing Diagram Option

The option "Show in timing diagram" is available only if the signal is named. Its box will be checked by default for any signal with a name displayed on the diagram. Any signal with this box checked will be displayed in the timing window when the simulation is running.

Note that the display status can be changed for any groups of selected signals using the Set Params command with any number of signals selected.

Omit from Report Option

The option "Omit from report" allows you to prevent this signal from appearing in netlists or other types of reports generated using the Report Generator. This is useful when signal traces have been added to the diagram for simulation purposes only and will not form part of the finished product.

Stuck Value Option

The option "Stuck value" allows you to prevent this signal from changing its simulation value, regardless of any devices driving the line. When this box is checked, the signal will retain whatever value it had at the time the Set Params command was selected. When the box is empty, the signal will be reevaluated based on the current output drives from devices connected to it. For more information, see Chapter 8, Simulation.

Editing the Signal Name

The signal name is shown in an editable text box. If this name is changed, all visible instances of the name will be changed. If the signal is currently unnamed and a name is entered here, the name will be associated with the signal but will not be displayed on the diagram. This is referred to as an "invisible name." An invisible name can be displayed on the diagram by clicking the pencil cursor anywhere along the signal line. More information on signal names is given below.

Signal Attributes

The Attributes box allows you to enter text data that will remain associated with the signal. See more information on attribute fields in Chapter 7, Devices.

Naming Signals

Names may contain any letters, numbers, or special characters that you can type on the keyboard, but they are limited to a length of 15 characters. The name associated with an object can be placed anywhere on the diagram and will be removed if the object is removed.

Use of Signal Names

Signal names are used to associate circuit and simulation data with a given signal trace on a diagram. In particular, the signal name is referenced by the following LogicWorks functions:

- The signal name is used in Report Generator output, such as netlists and simulation data reports.

- The signal name can be used to logically interconnect traces.

- The signal name is used as a label in the timing diagram for simulation output.

- When creating an internal circuit for a macro device, the signal name is used to associate signals with pins on the device symbol.

Creating a Signal Name

Enter name mode either by selecting the Name menu item from the Edit menu or by clicking on the pencil icon in the tool palette:

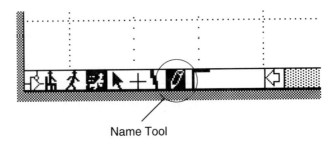

Name Tool

Note that once Name is selected, the pointer changes to the pencil cursor.

Press and hold the mouse button with the tip of the pencil positioned anywhere along a signal line except within 5 screen dots of a device. As long as you hold down the mouse button, an I-beam cursor will track the mouse movements. The signal name text will start at the position where you release the button. Type the desired name and press ⟨←Enter⟩ or click the mouse button anywhere. This is illustrated below.

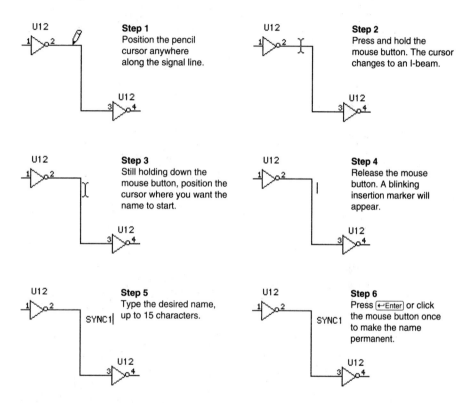

Step 1
Position the pencil cursor anywhere along the signal line.

Step 2
Press and hold the mouse button. The cursor changes to an I-beam.

Step 3
Still holding down the mouse button, position the cursor where you want the name to start.

Step 4
Release the mouse button. A blinking insertion marker will appear.

Step 5
Type the desired name, up to 15 characters.

Step 6
Press ⟨←Enter⟩ or click the mouse button once to make the name permanent.

LogicWorks recognizes two special signal names, "0" and "1". Any signal so named will be immediately set to a low or high value, respectively. These names may be applied to any number of signals. No special significance is ascribed to any other names. Any named signal will be displayed in the timing diagram by default, except for signals named "0" and "1". The timing display status can be changed using the Set Params command on the signal.

Invisible Signal Names

LogicWorks allows you to assign and edit signal names in a circuit without making them visible on the diagram. This process can be used to assign names that cannot be conveniently placed on the diagram, or that are needed for report generation purposes only. Signals with invisible names are *not* connected by name, except for invisible names created by a Signal Connector device, as described above.

Creating an Invisible Name

An invisible name is created or edited by selecting the desired signal line, then selecting the Set Params command from the Options menu (Ctrl-i). The Parameters box has an editable text box for the signal name. If the name is shown on the diagram, changing it here will change all displayed occurrences of it.

Making an Invisible Name Visible

An invisible signal name can be made visible simply by clicking the pencil cursor anywhere along the signal line. When the mouse button is released, the name will be positioned at that point.

Removing or Editing a Name

Removing a Name

A device or signal name can be removed by using Zap mode, described above. If the signal has been named in multiple locations, Zap removes the name only at the location Zapped.

Editing a Name

The name can be changed simply by clicking on the signal name with the pencil cursor and entering the new name. Alternatively, a name can be edited by selecting the signal and choosing Set Params. Changing the name in the Set Params box or at any one location on the diagram will change all visible occurrences of it.

Moving a Name

A device or signal name can be moved by selecting the arrow cursor, pressing and holding the mouse button on the name, and dragging it to the desired new position. Pin numbers cannot be repositioned.

Multiple Naming of Signals

A signal name can appear in up to 100 positions along the length of a signal line. To add a new position, simply use the normal naming procedure given in the section on signal naming.

- Select name mode.

- Click and drag anywhere along the signal line.

- With the mouse button pressed, move to the desired position for the name.

- Release the mouse button.

A new copy of the signal's name will appear at this point followed by a flashing cursor. To accept the name, simply click the mouse button once or press ⏎Enter. If you edit any occurrence of a name along a signal segment, all other occurrences will be updated to reflect the new name.

Any occurrence of a signal name can be removed using Zap mode. If you remove the last visible name from a signal segment, the logical connectivity to other like-named signals is removed.

Pin Numbering

Pin numbers may contain one to four characters and are always positioned adjacent to the associated pin.

Uses of Pin Numbers

Pin numbers are used only for labeling purposes and have no particular connectivity or simulation significance to LogicWorks. Pin numbers are not checked for duplicates or other invalid usage. Pin numbers placed on a diagram will be used in creating a netlist (see the Report Generator manual), and will appear when the circuit is printed. If a pin is unnumbered, it will appear in the netlist as "?".

Placing a Pin Number

If the mouse button is pressed with the tip of the pencil positioned on a signal line within 5 screen dots of a device, a blinking insertion bar will appear exactly where the signal joins the device. You cannot set the text position for pin numbers. Type the desired one- to four-character number and press ⏎Enter, or click the mouse button anywhere, to make the number permanent. See the sequential numbering option discussed below under "Auto-Naming Features."

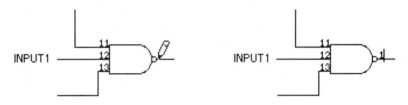

Default Pin Numbers

A device type may have default pin numbers associated with it which will appear when the device is first created. These pin numbers are not permanent and can be edited or removed by the techniques discussed in this section. The LogicWorks primitive devices (in the Gates and Devices menus) have no default pin numbers, so if pin numbers are needed, they must be added manually when these devices are used. PROM and PLA devices created from within LogicWorks can have default pin numbers added using the PROM/PLA edit dialog box (see the Chapter 9, PROM and PLA Devices). Devices in a library can have default pin numbers assigned to them using the DevEditor module (see Chapter 12, The Device Editor).

Auto-Naming Features

Two features are available to simplify the naming of groups of related signals, devices, and pins. These features are activated by holding down Ctrl, Alt, or ⇧Shift while selecting the signal to be named with the pencil cursor.

Auto-Alignment

If Ctrl is held down while the signal is selected, the text insertion point will be positioned horizontally aligned with the last signal name that was entered.

The vertical position is determined by the vertical position of the line that was clicked on. This feature works only with signal names, not with devices or pin numbers.

Auto–Name Generation

If Alt is held down while a signal, device, or pin is selected, a new name is generated automatically for this item. The new name is the same as the last one entered, except that the numeric part of the name is increased by one. If the previously entered name did not have a numeric part, then a "1" will be appended to it. If ⇧Shift is pressed at the same time, the number will be decremented instead of incremented.

Bus Naming

The previous two features can be used in combination to perform easy naming of bussed signals. The normal symbol standard in LogicWorks is to position the highest numbers at the top, so you can choose either of the following procedures:

■ Number the topmost line in the group (for example, D7) using the normal naming technique, described above, then hold down Ctrl, Alt, and ⇧Shift while clicking on successive lower-numbered lines.

■ Number the bottommost line in the group (for example, D0) using the normal naming technique described above, then hold down Ctrl and Alt while clicking on successive higher-numbered lines.

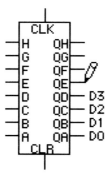

Note that when you select each successive line, the new name appears automatically, and you can go right on to the next line.

7

Devices

This chapter provides information on the editing and simulation characteristics of devices.

Classes of Devices

For the purposes of this section, device types in LogicWorks can be divided into four groups:

- **Primitive devices.** The simulation characteristics of these devices are determined by program code internal to LogicWorks, although the symbols can be modified using the DevEditor module. The primitive devices are contained in the Gates, Generic, and IO libraries. The I/O devices are a special case in that they cannot be modified in any way, since they must be redrawn in a number of different states.

- **Macro devices.** These have simulation characteristics (if any) that are determined by an internal circuit. Most of the libraries provided with LogicWorks contain macro devices. It is possible to create a "symbol-only" macro device with no internal circuit and which therefore has no simulation function. The analog devices provided with LogicWorks are examples of these. If you do not plan to use the LogicWorks simulator, you can substantially decrease the size of your circuit files by using the NOSIMLOAD option in the Setup file. This prevents loading of internal macro circuits. See the section "Setup File Format" in the Appendix for more information.

■ **User-defined primitive types created in LogicWorks.** These behave like primitive devices from a delay point of view, but their logic is determined by the user. These types include the PROM, PLA, RAM, and Connector types. These devices are created within LogicWorks but are saved in a library file like the other types. They can be used just like any other device and made part of a macro device, if desired, using the DevEditor module. See Chapter 9, PROM and PLA Devices.

■ **Pseudo-devices with special schematic functions.** These include Signal Connectors and Page Connectors. Although these are not devices, from a circuit functional point of view, they are treated internally as special devices, and any editing features that can be applied to other types can also be applied to these.

Editing Devices

Naming the Device

NOTE: In this manual, we use the term *device name* to refer to the character string that identifies a unique device in the circuit. Typical device names might be "U23", "C4", and "IC12A". This is distinct from the *type name* used to distinguish the type definition read from a device library. Typical type names are "74LS138", "MC68000L8", and "SPDT Switch".

Device names may contain any letters, numbers, or special characters that you can type on the keyboard but are restricted to a maximum length of 15 characters. The name associated with an object can be placed anywhere on the diagram and will be removed if the object is removed.

Enter name mode either by selecting the Name menu item from the Edit menu or by clicking on the pencil icon in the tool palette:

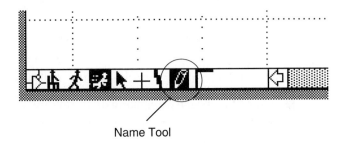

Name Tool

Note that once Name is selected, the pointer changes to the pencil cursor.

Press and hold the mouse button with the tip of the pencil positioned inside a device symbol. As long as you hold down the mouse button, an I-beam cursor will track the mouse movements. The device name text will start at the position where you release the button. Type the desired name and press ⌐←Enter⌐, or click the mouse button anywhere. This sequence of steps is illustrated below.

Position the pencil cursor anywhere inside the device symbol.

Click and hold the mouse button. The cursor changes to an I-beam.

Still holding down the mouse button, position the cursor where you want the name to start.

Release the mouse button. A blinking insertion marker will appear.

U123|

Type the desired name, up to 15 characters.

U123

Press ⌐Enter⌐ or click the mouse button once to make the name permanent.

Once a name is placed, it can be repositioned by dragging it using the arrow cursor or removed using the lightning bolt cursor in Zap mode. The device name will be removed automatically if the device is removed.

Removing Devices

Devices can be removed by either of two methods:

■ Select the device by clicking on it (holding down ⬆Shift if it is a switch or other input device) and then pressing ←Backspace or select the Clear command from the Edit menu.

■ Enter Zap mode by selecting the Zap command or clicking on the Zap icon in the tool palette, then click on the device you wish to remove.

WARNING: Both of these operations are irreversible!

Moving Devices

Devices can be moved by clicking and dragging to the desired new position. If more than one device is selected, all the devices and all signals connecting between them (whether selected or not) will be moved. Signal lines will be adjusted to maintain right angles at points where moving signal lines intersect with nonmoving ones.

Entering Attributes

LogicWorks allows an arbitrary string of text up to 32,000 characters to be associated with any device or signal. This feature is provided primarily for use in creating SPICE output files. LogicWorks does not enforce any rules for how this text must be formatted, but some rules must be followed for correct operation with the Report module. For more information on attributes, see Chapter 13, Creating Text Reports.

Device Libraries

The prototypes for LogicWorks device types are stored in data files called device libraries. An individual library may contain up to 100 device types, and LogicWorks allows you to have up to 31 libraries open at any one time. Libraries can be opened and closed using the Open Lib and Close Lib commands from the Libraries menu, or using the Setup file.

For each device type in a library the following data is stored:

- General information on the type, such as number of pins, number of inputs, number of outputs, type name, default delay, position, orientation, and type of each pin.

- A picture representing the symbol for this type.

- The internal circuit for the device. This is omitted for primitive devices or for macro devices having no simulation function.

How Devices Are Created and Stored

Libraries are created and modified using the DevEditor module, which is described in Chapter 12, The Device Editor. This section provides a brief outline of the steps necessary to create your own device. Refer to Chapter 12 for a complete example.

The DevEditor module takes information from the following three sources to create a device data entry acceptable to LogicWorks:

- If the device is to have an internal circuit, the circuit data must be in an open LogicWorks circuit window. There are very few restrictions on this circuit except that is must have a named signal (not connected by name) for each external pin connection. Because the circuit becomes invisible, it does not make sense to include any I/O devices.

- The symbol you wish to use for your device can be drawn right in the DevEditor window. The only restriction on the symbol is that the pin positions must fall on a 5-point grid.

- Using the mouse, you must indicate to the DevEditor the position, direction, and pin number of each pin connection on your device.

The 7400 Series

The 7400 series libraries include devices with full simulation implemented. These are functional models only: We have not attempted to match the delay characteristics of these devices, only the internal logic. These devices are LogicWorks macros, that is, the devices are internally made up of primitive devices and PLAs. PLAs are used wherever possible for the sake of memory efficiency, but this means that delay characteristics of the devices may be different from what you might derive from the circuit in a data book. The Set Params command in LogicWorks can be used to determine the delay along the longest path through the device (see below for more information). This should be taken into account when determining clock rates for circuit simulations.

The LSI and Analog Libraries

The remaining libraries include devices in symbol-only form. In LogicWorks, all pins on these devices will behave as inputs for simulation purposes. If you wish to create a simulation model to go with any of these, you can attach a circuit to any symbol using the Internal Circuit command from the DevEditor menu. See Chapter 12, The Device Editor, for more information.

Multigate Packages

In the 7400 libraries, device types having multiple gates per package, such as a 74LS04, are represented in two ways:

- Using a single device symbol with multiple gates enclosed in a rectangle. Because this is only a single LogicWorks device symbol, all the gates must be located together on the diagram and a single device name applied to the symbol will apply to all gates.

- Using a number of separate types, one for each section of the device. In this format it is the user's responsibility to ensure that gates are allocated correctly to packages. For netlisting and report generation purposes, any collection of devices having the same name are assumed to be part of the same device. In the current version of LogicWorks, no automatic checking is done for overlapping or unused pins.

SPICE Interface

Many simulation packages have specific requirements for the order in which pins are specified in a netlist. In LogicWorks, the pin order used in generating a report file is determined by the order in which the pins are defined in the DevEditor, that is, the order they appear in the pin list.

SPICE-based simulators normally use the pin order defined in the original Berkeley SPICE implementation for discrete components. The LogicWorks Discretes library contains symbols for discrete components with the number and order of pins specified to match the common device models available in SPICE-based simulators. Any of these symbols, then, should produce correct results when interfacing to simulators using the standard pin order. Other analog simulators are not supported in LogicWorks.

Device Delay

In symbols with simulation, all internal devices are left with their default delay of 1 unit. Crude adjustments to the delay can be made in LogicWorks by selecting the device (by clicking on it) and using the Set Params command from the Options menu. Any change in this delay setting increments or decrements all internal devices by the same amount, so the exact effect depends on the circuit logic.

The Set Params display shows the delays associated with the shortest and longest paths through the device, as in the following example:

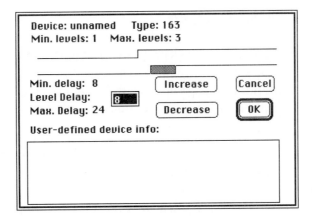

In this case, the nominal delay for the 163 has been set to 8 units. Assuming no unusual adjustments have been made to the internal circuit, this means that the delay through each internal primitive device is 8 units. The "Min. levels" and "Max. levels" items give the number of primitive devices along the shortest and longest signal paths through the device, and "Min. delay" and "Max. delay" show the corresponding delays. Refer to other parts of this manual for more information on Set Params and the delay calculation.

Setting One-Shot and Clock Parameters

LogicWorks allows you to set parameters for One-Shot and Clock Generator devices internal to macros (such as the one-shots). Select the device by clicking on it and select Set Params from the Options menu. You will be prompted for each clock or one-shot in the macro, then for the overall delay for the device.

Modifying Libraries

The DevEditor module allows you to replace the picture or the internal circuit for any device type in a library. Do not modify the original libraries supplied with LogicWorks; work only with copies. Note that modifying a device type in a library has no effect on circuits that have already used that type. LogicWorks stores all types used with each circuit and keeps no reference to the original library.

Pin Numbering

Most of the symbols provided in these libraries include pin numbers, which are added to the pins automatically when LogicWorks reads a device from the library. The pin numbers can be changed in LogicWorks after the device is created using the pin-numbering facility (Name command), or the defaults can be changed in the libraries using the DevEditor module.

Sources of Information and Disclaimer

The device simulations are derived from functional specifications and other data in the following data books: *The TTL Data Book for Design Engineers,* Second Edition, Texas Instruments; *The TTL Data Book,* Volume 2, 1985, Texas Instruments; *ALS/AS Logic Data Book,* 1986, Texas Instruments; *LSI Logic Data Book,* 1986, Texas Instruments; *Intel Component Data Catalog; Motorola CMOS Data; Motorola Microprocessors Data Manual,* and others. Because we depend on these sources for information and do not have the resources to purchase and test every chip ourselves, we cannot accept any responsibility for the accuracy of these simulations. In cases where there are logic differences between LS and S, ALS, AS, HC, (or other) devices, we have based our symbols on the LS logic.

8
Simulation

This chapter provides more-detailed information on the simulation capabilities of LogicWorks and on interpreting and editing in the timing window.

General Information on Simulation

LogicWorks has the ability to perform a realistic simulation of any digital circuit. Obviously, though, any simulation of any system must be limited in detail and must make certain assumptions. In particular, when simulating digital circuits, it must be understood that real circuits are never completely "digital" in nature, and in fact have many "analog" properties which affect how they operate. LogicWorks is primarily intended to assist with the logical design of a circuit, and does not take into account factors such as line loading, power supply noise, rise and fall times, or output drive. As more of these factors are taken into account, the simulation becomes slower and less interactive, which defeats the purpose for which LogicWorks was created.

For more information on how the simulation is performed, see "Inside LogicWorks" in the Appendix.

Time Units

LogicWorks uses 32-bit integer arithmetic to calculate all time values used in the simulation. It is usually convenient to think of these values as being in nanoseconds, but the actual interpretation is left up to the user.

For most primitive devices, the default delay value is 1 unit, but the delay can be set to any integer value from 0 to 32,767. Macro devices inherit their delay characteristics from their internal circuit, although rough adjustments can be made using the Set Params command.

Effect of Zero Delay

A delay value of 0 is permitted in a LogicWorks device, but this setting should be used only with an understanding of how the simulation is implemented because it can result in unexpected side effects. For more information on this, see "Inside LogicWorks" in the Appendix.

Signal States

LogicWorks uses 13 different device output states in order to track conditions within your circuit. These states can be broken into three groups, as follows.

Forcing States (denoted by suffix .F):

```
LOW.F
HIGH.F
DONT01.F
DONT0Z.F
DONT1Z.F
CONF.F
```

Resistive States (denoted by suffix .R).

```
LOW.R
HIGH.R
DONT01.R
DONT0Z.R
DONT1Z.R
CONF.R
```

High Impedance:

```
HIGHZ
```

Note that the forcing/resistive distinction is used only to resolve conflicts between multiple outputs connected to the same signal. The final value stored or displayed for a given signal line can only be one of five possibilities:

```
LOW
HIGH
DONT
CONF
HIGHZ
```

Stuck-At Levels

The LogicWorks simulator implements "stuck-at" levels to assist in setting initial simulation states, testing for faults, and so on. When a signal is stuck, it will not change state, regardless of changes in devices driving the line. The stuck status can only be cleared by one of the following user actions:

- Pressing (Spacebar) while viewing the signal using the probe tool in the tool palette.

- Clicking off the Stuck Value checkbox in the Set Params dialog box.

When the stuck status is set, the signal will retain the value it had at that time until some user action forces a change. When the stuck status is removed, the signal will return to the value determined by the devices driving the line.

Resolution of Multiple Device Outputs

The DONT0Z and DONT1Z values are used primarily to handle cases of open-collector or open-emitter devices with unknown inputs (more information is provided below). Most other types of devices produce the DONT01 output when a value cannot be calculated.

In cases where two or more device outputs are connected and each one drives the line with a different value, the following rules are used to resolve the actual value on the line.

■ The forcing/resistive distinction is used only to resolve outputs from multiple devices. The final value used for display and simulation purposes is one of the forcing values or HIGHZ.

■ A forcing drive always overrides a resistive drive or HIGHZ (that is, the signal takes on the value of the forcing drive, ignoring all resistive drives and HIGHZs).

■ A resistive drive always overrides HIGHZ.

■ DONT0Z.F and LOW.F produce LOW.

■ DONT1Z.F and HIGH.F produce HIGH.

■ Any other combination of conflicting forcing drives produces CONF.

■ DONT0Z.R and LOW.R produce LOW.

■ DONT1Z.R and HIGH.R produce HIGH.

■ Any other combination of conflicting resistive drives produces CONF.

Resistive Versus Forcing Drive

All primitive devices in LogicWorks output a forcing-drive level except the Pullup Resistor and Resistor types. The function of the Resistor device is to convert a forcing drive on one side into a resistive drive on the other. This can be used to modify the output of any existing device type by placing a resistor in series with it. Note that LogicWorks does not model analog properties of devices, so the resistor does not have a resistance value in the analog sense. In particular, there is no interaction between resistor and capacitor symbols to produce delay in lines. The delay effect can be simulated by setting a delay value for the resistor.

Description of Signal States

The High and Low states are the normal ones expected in a binary circuit but are not sufficient to realistically simulate circuit operation, so the High Impedance, Don't Know, and Conflict states are added. There will always be some cases where the simulation will not correctly mimic what would appear in a real circuit, and some of these cases are discussed below. In particular, if a circuit takes advantage of some analog property of a specific device, such as inputs that float high, known state at power-up, or input hysteresis, it will generally not simulate correctly.

High Impedance

This state ("Z" on a logic probe) is used for cases when no device output is driving a given signal line. This may occur for an unconnected input, or for a disabled "three-state" or "open-collector" type device. If a device input is in the High Impedance state, it is treated as unknown for the purposes of simulation, even though in a real circuit the device may assume a High or Low state, depending on the circuit technology used.

Don't Know

The "Don't Know" state ("X" on a logic probe) results when the simulator cannot determine the output of a device. This may occur, for example, when an input is unconnected or the output from a previous device is unknown. The Don't Know signal will be propagated through the circuit, showing the potential effects of that condition.

The Don't Know state is used in LogicWorks in cases where the actual result in a real circuit would depend on the circuit technology used, on random chance, or on analog properties of the device not predictable using a strictly digital simulation. For example, if the following ring oscillator circuit is created in LogicWorks, all signals will be permanently unknown, since each depends on the previous one, which is also unknown. In actual hardware, this circuit may oscillate, or may settle into an intermediate logic level, which would not be defined in a digital circuit.

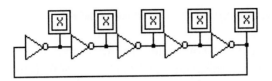

For the purposes of simulation, all circuits must have some provision for initialization to a known state. In most cases, circuits can be initialized using the Clear Unknowns command, described elsewhere in the manual. Alternatively, circuitry can be added to allow a reset to be done, as in the following modification to the ring oscillator:

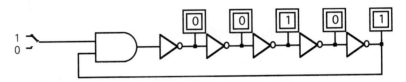

A problem arises in simulating circuits with multiple open-collector devices, such as a bus line, illustrated below:

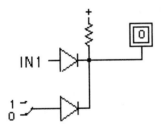

In this circuit the upper device has an unconnected input at IN1 and therefore outputs a Don't Know value. The lower device has a low input and therefore outputs a low value. To correctly resolve this situation, the simulator needs to distinguish between a Don't Know output from a normal "totem-pole" type output and a Don't Know from an open-collector, open-drain, or other single-drive output. In this case, the upper device will produce a DONT0Z output that resolves correctly to a LOW on the output regardless of the state of IN1, using the rules described above.

Conflict

The Conflict state ("C" on a logic probe) results when two device outputs are connected and are of different or unknown states according to the rules described above.

The following timing diagram shows how the various signal states are displayed.

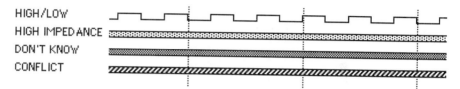

Circuit Window Simulation Controls

Several items in the tool palette at the lower-left corner of each circuit window are used to control the simulator.

Controlling Simulation Speed

The simulation can be single-stepped or walked (2 time steps per second) using the tool palette on either the circuit or timing windows. Each click on the Pause icon will cause the next event time to be simulated.

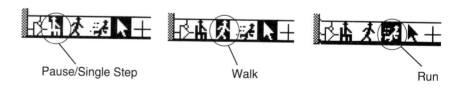

Pause/Single Step   Walk   Run

Probe Tool

The probe tool in the tool palette allows you to interactively examine and change values on individual signals on the circuit diagram. When the probe tip is clicked and held on a signal line, the cursor will show the current value on the signal and track changes that occur as the simulation progresses.

Signal Probe

Only the signal under the cursor at the time of the click is examined; moving the mouse while the button is pressed does not change the signal being viewed.

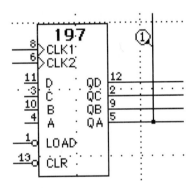

While the mouse button is held down, you can press keys on the keyboard to inject new values onto the signal, as follows:

0	LOW.F
1	HIGH.F
X	DONT01.F
C	CONF.F
Z	HIGHZ
L	LOW.F stuck
H	HIGH.F stuck
Spacebar	Unstick

Device Simulation Characteristics

Input Signal Values

For all device types except switches, signal values High Impedance and Conflict are treated as Don't Know when applied to a device input. When a device is first created, all input signals take the High Impedance state and outputs are set accordingly, normally to the Don't Know state. An unused input pin, then, will appear as an unknown input to a device, which may affect its output level. As with real circuits, all unused inputs should be connected to a high or low level as appropriate. This can be done by naming the pin either "0" or "1" (using Name from the Edit menu), using a power or ground symbol, or by using a pullup resistor to set a high level. See more information on logic states in other parts of this chapter.

Setup and Hold Times

All standard device types having an edge-triggered clock—such as the D-type and JK-type flip-flops, register, and shift register—have an effective setup time of 1 unit and a hold time of 0 units. That is, if the data and clock inputs change simultaneously, the old value of the data input will be used. Setup and hold times cannot be set by the user.

Device Delay

All primitive (user- or pre-defined) devices with inputs and outputs have an integer delay value associated with them. The initial delay value is set to 1 when the device is created, but this can be changed later using Set Params from the Options menu. This delay applies whenever any input change causes an output change. There is no provision in the built-in simulation models for different delay values between different combinations of pins, or for different values on low-to-high and high-to-low transitions. The Clock Osc, Switch, Probe, Hex Keyboard, and Hex Display devices have no delay characteristic.

A macro device has no inherent delay, since its delay is determined by its internal circuitry. When you Set Params on a macro device, the display will indicate the delay through the shortest and longest paths through the device. When you adjust the delay value for the macro, the delay of all internal devices is incremented or decremented by an equal amount.

Setting the Delay

Set the delay for a device by either of the following methods:

- Select the device (by clicking the mouse button with the pointer positioned on the device icon) and then choose Set Params from the Options menu.

- Hold down [Alt] and click the pointer on the device.

A dialog box will appear, allowing you to increase or decrease the delay value by clicking one of two buttons. The minimum delay value is 0 and the maximum is 32,767. When the delay setting for a macro device is changed, the delays for all internal devices are changed by the same amount.

Primitive Devices

For a primitive (built-in) device with a delay characteristic, the following box is displayed:

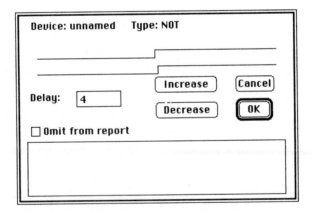

All devices that have a delay characteristic have a default delay of 1, but this can be changed to any value in the range 0 to 32,767. Delay changes immediately affect the simulation in progress. A delay value of 0 can create side effects in the way the circuit is simulated.

Macro Devices with an Internal Circuit

If the selected device is a macro device with an internal circuit, changing its delay increments the delays of all internal devices having non-zero delays by the same amount, so long as they don't go below 0 or above 32,767. That is, if you change the delay setting for the macro device from 5 to 10, all internal devices will have their delay incremented by 5. If this increment causes the delay for an individual device to go outside the allowable limit, then it is set to the limit. Internal devices that have an initial delay setting of 0 are not adjusted. This allows devices to be added to change the logic of a circuit without changing its delay characteristics. The delay dialog box for a macro device displays more information than one for a primitive device:

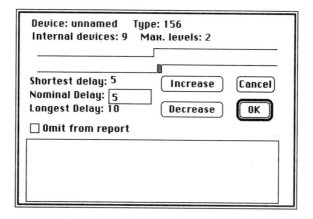

Note that the delay value that appears for the macro device is a nominal value, since all simulation characteristics are determined by the settings of the internal devices. Before displaying this dialog box, the program determines the shortest and longest paths through the device from any input pin to any output pin. The "Internal devices" item is a count of the total number of devices internal to this macro. The "Max. levels" number is a count of the devices encountered along the longest path through the device from an input to an output. The "Min. delay" and "Max. delay" values are the total delays along the shortest and longest paths, given the actual delay settings for the internal devices. These numbers are updated as the nominal delay setting is changed.

The input/output transition display shows a grayed area between the time of the shortest and longest path delays.

Symbol-Only Macro Devices

A macro device with no internal circuit has no delay characteristic, so a simplified Parameter box is displayed:

```
┌─────────────────────────────────────────────────┐
│  ┌──────────────────────────────────────────┐   │
│  │  Device: unnamed    Type: 80286    ┌──────┐ │
│  │                                    │  OK  │ │
│  │  ☐ Omit from report                └──────┘ │
│  │  Device attributes:                [Cancel] │
│  │  ┌────────────────────────────────────────┐ │
│  │  │                                        │ │
│  │  │                                        │ │
│  │  │                                        │ │
│  │  │                                        │ │
│  │  └────────────────────────────────────────┘ │
│  └──────────────────────────────────────────────┘
└─────────────────────────────────────────────────┘
```

Clock Devices

When a clock is created, it has default high and low times of 10, giving a period of 20 with a duty cycle of 50%. For more information on setting clock times, see the "Clock Osc" section in Chapter 10, Primitive Devices.

One-Shot Devices

When a one-shot is created, it has a default delay time of 1 and a pulse duration of 10. For more information on setting delay and duration times, see the "One-Shot" section in Chapter 10, Primitive Devices.

Omit from Report

When this option is set, the selected device will not appear in any netlists, component lists, or other output from the Report module. This can be used, for example, to effectively hide devices that are added to a schematic for simulation purposes only and would not form part of a finished product.

The Timing Diagram

A timing diagram for your circuit will be created in the timing window as the simulation progresses. All signals which have been named (except "0" and "1") will be shown unless you have explicitly turned off the display flag by selecting the signal and issuing a Set Params command from the Options menu.

Any structural change in the circuit will cause the diagram to be erased and the simulation to progress with the new circuit parameters. The timing window can be moved on the screen and resized as needed to display the desired number of signals. The display resolution for the timing diagram defaults to 2 screen dots per time unit, but this can be altered using the Timing Options command from the Options menu. For more information on this command, see Chapter 11, Menu Reference. Note that the lower the display resolution, the more memory is used internally, because enough data must be stored to redraw the timing diagram as needed.

WARNING: Drawing state changes on a signal line that is being driven by a logic device in your circuit will result in a very confused simulation. Changes entered in the timing diagram override the current output state of a device until that device outputs a new change in value.

The Parts of the Timing Window

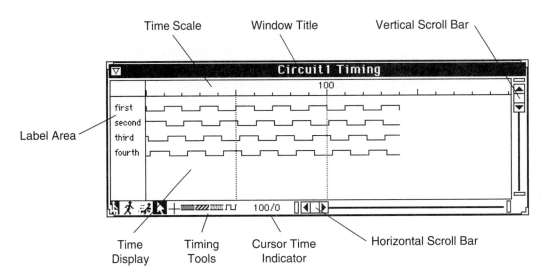

Time Scale   Window Title   Vertical Scroll Bar

Label Area

Time Display   Timing Tools   Cursor Time Indicator   Horizontal Scroll Bar

Window Title

The title bar displays the title of the timing window for the current circuit—that is, the name of the current circuit with the word "Timing" appended.

Label Area

The list of names of the signal lines that were labeled in the current circuit are displayed in the left-hand margin of the timing window. Selected labels and their corresponding timing signals can be repositioned within the list by clicking on the desired names (using ⟨⇧Shift⟩ to select multiple items) and dragging the outlined box vertically to its new location. Releasing the mouse button will cause the list to be revised with the labels and traces in their new positions.

Time Scale

Located just below the timing window's title bar, the time scale is used to aid in referencing state changes in the signal lines displayed below it. The scale is dependent on the timing resolution set using the Timing Options command. The time scale is also used to set insertion points and selection intervals for use in editing functions.

Timing Tools

The timing tools are a series of five tools used in editing the signal lines displayed in the timing window when the circuit is paused. New states can be created and modified only in the future (to the right of the point in time where the simulation was halted). The tools are located left of the cursor time indicator at the bottom of the window.

Time Display

The time display is the area of the window where the newly created states (when paused) and waveforms of the current circuit (when running) are displayed. The display is bordered by the label area to the left and the time scale above.

Cursor Time Indicator

This displays the time at which the cursor is located in the time display. The indicator will normally show the present time of the cursor in reference to the time scale. But when the cursor is in point mode and the mouse button is depressed and dragged, the indicator will display the time difference relative to the point where the mouse button was first pressed.

Horizontal Scroll Bar

Dragging the horizontal scroll bar allows the user to display objects to the right or to the left of the present viewing area. In the case of the time display, it will allow viewing of the future (to the right), the present, and the past (to the left) portions of waveforms labeled in the current circuit. The horizontal scroll bar is disabled when the simulation is running.

Vertical Scroll Bar

Dragging the vertical scroll bar allows the user to display objects above or below the present viewing area. In the case of the time display, it will display the signal labels and their corresponding timing signal above or below the ones currently displayed.

Function of the Timing Tools

High/Low $+$

- ■ Creates the High or Low signal state, depending on the vertical position of the cursor after dragging and releasing the mouse button.

- ■ Modifies the time at which the state occurs by clicking on, and dragging horizontally, the vertical edge of the signal, and is set at the time where the mouse button is released.

- ■ Modifies the state by clicking on the horizontal edge and dragging up or down. The new state is set when the mouse button is released.

Don't Know ▨

- ■ Creates the Don't Know signal state.

- ■ Modifies the time at which the state occurs by clicking on and dragging horizontally the vertical edge of the signal, and is set at the time where the mouse button is released.

HighZ ▨

- ■ Creates the High Impedance signal state.

- ■ Modifies the time at which the state occurs by clicking on and dragging horizontally the vertical edge of the signal, and is set at the time where the mouse button is released

Conflict ▨

- ■ Creates the Conflict signal state.

- ■ Modifies the time at which the state occurs by clicking on and dragging horizontally the vertical edge of the signal, and is set at the time where the mouse button is released.

Insertion ⊓

- ■ Inserts only High/Low signal states between previously created states.

Selecting Data for Edit Operations

The following steps must be carried out before selection operations can be performed:

- The circuit must be paused. To pause, either click on the Pause icon (the figure sitting in a chair) in the tool palette in the bottom-left corner of the window or click anywhere in the timing window.

- The cursor must be in point mode. If not already in point mode, click on the pointer icon in the tool palette. The cursor changes to the arrow.

There are two ways to select labels and their corresponding timing signals:

Method One

You can select one or more labels and then set the selection interval by following these steps:

- **Selecting the labels.** Clicking on the desired label in the label area will cause the label to be highlighted and selected. To select more than one label, press ⟨⇧Shift⟩ while clicking on the labels.

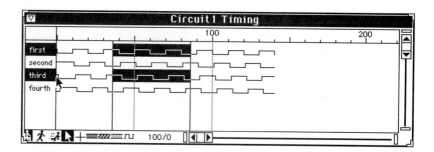

- **Set selection intervals.** Press and hold the mouse button in the time scale at either the beginning or end of the selection interval. A flashing vertical line with arrows pointing in opposite directions will appear. When you drag the mouse, the single line will break into two vertical lines, one remaining at the point where the mouse button was pressed, the other will move horizontally with the cursor. Regardless of the direction the cursor is moved, the arrows on the two lines always point toward each other, and the area between the lines will be selected when the mouse button is released. When the mouse button is released, the selection interval is set, and two vertical lines appear, one at the point where the mouse button was pressed, the other where it was released. The timing signal within the selection interval will be highlighted in time display for any of the signal labels that were selected.

Method Two

You can simultaneously select a group of signals and set the selection interval by doing the following:

- Click and drag the mouse in the time display. This draws a selection box in the time display. The group of signals you wish to select should be within the box. The selection interval will be the area between the right and left edges of the box. When the button is released, the signal states within the box and the time interval lines will be highlighted.

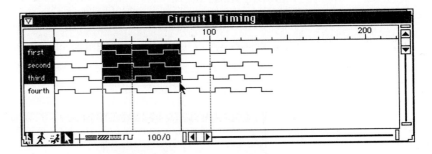

Changing the Selection

Clicking anywhere in the time display will deselect the labels and selection interval. The selection interval may also be adjusted to cover a different time duration by repositioning the selected interval. Clicking and holding down the mouse button at the top of either the starting interval or the ending interval will cause the the two flashing lines with arrows to reappear.

The selected line will now follow the cursor while the other remains stationary. When the button is released, the new selection interval is set.

NOTE: Be careful to click exactly on the vertical interval lines. If you miss, the selection interval will be reset.

The selection operations in the timing window are independent of the operation in the circuit window.

Edit Menu Functions

The Edit menu functions Cut, Copy, Paste, Clear, and Duplicate can be used to edit the timing window. The simulation must be paused to use the timing editing functions. The following rules apply:

Cut

- You can cut signal states from the future only—that is, to the right of the point where the timing has paused.

Paste

- You can paste signal states into the future only.

- Either an insertion point or selection interval must be set.

- Setting the paste selection interval is the same operation as setting the interval in the selection of signals described above.

- Set the paste insertion point by clicking once in the time scale where the signal states are to be pasted. A single dark vertical line will appear to represent the insertion point. The insertion point can be set only in the future.

- If a paste selection interval is set, only the events that will fit into that interval will be pasted. Any events that fall outside the selected interval will be ignored.

■ If an insertion point is set, all signal events with matching signal names to the right of the insertion point will be moved forward in time by the length of the new events that are pasted.

Duplicate

■ The ending interval line must be in the future.

Clear

■ You can clear only the signal states that are in the future.

Copy

■ No restrictions, except that a selection must be made before Copy is invoked.

9

PROM and PLA Devices

This chapter provides details on creating and using PROM and PLA devices with user-specified data. Note that the PROM/PLA facility can also be used to create simple symbols for schematic purposes with no simulation functions.

General Description of PROM and PLA Types

LogicWorks allows you to define your own logic device types by simply entering the device truth table (PROM form), or by listing input combinations which will produce a desired high or low output (PLA form). This type of specification has a number of advantages:

■ There is no need to design a network of gates which will produce the desired outputs.

■ A single device can replace a larger number of standard logic components.

■ You can verify the correctness of data to program expensive PROM or PLA chips.

PROM Data Format

For the purposes of simulation in LogicWorks, a PROM (Programmable Read Only Memory) is defined as a device having N inputs (from 1 to 12) and M outputs (from 1 to 16), and having 2^N storage locations, each containing M bits. Each different input combination selects one of the storage locations, the contents of which appear on the output lines. The number of storage locations required doubles for each input bit added, so PROM organization is practical for only a relatively small number of inputs. The advantage of the PROM is that any arbitrary Boolean function can be represented simply by storing the truth table for the function in the appropriate storage locations.

PLA Data Format

In LogicWorks, a PLA (Programmable Logic Array) consists of a group of AND gates feeding into a single OR (active high) or NOR (active low) gate for each output bit. Each AND-gate input is connected to either an input bit, the inverse of an input bit, or constant high. By selectively making these input connections it is possible to determine which input combinations will produce 0s or 1s in the outputs.

The input connections required to implement simple logic functions can generally be determined "by eye," whereas more complex logic must be reduced using Karnaugh maps, the Quine-McClusky method, or other more advanced design techniques. These methods are discussed in numerous circuit design textbooks and will not be covered here. LogicWorks has the capability of reading device data produced by external logic minimization programs.

Creating a PROM or PLA Device

Select New PROM or PLA from the Options menu. The following dialog box will appear:

```
┌─────────────────────────────────────────────────┐
│                                                   │
│   Type Name          Type of Device               │
│   ┌──────────────┐    ◉ PLA Active High           │
│   │              │    ○ PLA Active Low            │
│                       ○ PROM Bitwise              │
│   Default Delay       ○ PROM Wordwise             │
│   ┌──────────────┐                                │
│   │ 1            │                                 │
│                                                   │
│   Inputs                                          │
│   ┌──────┐    [Specify Inputs]   [Read File]      │
│   │      │                                        │
│   Outputs                                         │
│   ┌──────┐    [Specify Outputs]  [Cancel]         │
│   │      │                        ┌─────────┐     │
│                                   │   OK    │     │
│                                   └─────────┘     │
│   ☐ Allow reload when inside macro                │
│                                                   │
└─────────────────────────────────────────────────┘
```

The Read File option allows you to select a disk file containing device data. When working with more complex PROM or PLA devices, it is desirable to create device data using an external software package, rather than having to do tedious logic manipulations by hand. For more information on the use of this feature, see "Reading an External PROM/PLA Data File" later in this chapter.

Completing the New PROM/PLA Dialog Box

To create a device manually, format information must be entered into this dialog box, as follows:

Type Name

Enter in this box the name you wish to associate with the new device type and press [Tab⇆] to move to the next box. This name will appear in the symbol and in the library menu.

Default Delay

This number must be between 0 and 32,767 and determines the default delay time for this device type. The actual delay for each device can be set using the Set Params command from the Options menu. Press ⟨Tab⟩ to move to the next box.

Inputs

This is the number of inputs on the new device type. For a PLA type, it must be between 1 and 64. For a PROM it must be between 1 and 12. Press ⟨Tab⟩ to move to the next box.

Outputs

This is the number of outputs on the new device type and must be between 1 and 16. Press ⟨Tab⟩ to continue.

Allow Reload When Inside Macro

This option is used primarily for creating macros of Programmable Logic Devices (PLDs). When this option is on, any macro device containing this PROM or PLA will be editable using the Edit Internals command. Normally this should be left off.

Once the above four items are entered, the Specify Inputs, Specify Outputs, and OK buttons will be highlighted. If you click on the OK button or press ⟨←Enter⟩ at this point, you will have an empty PLA device with Active High outputs. "Empty" in this case means that no terms are associated with each output bit, so all output bits would be 0 regardless of the inputs. Assuming this is not what you want, you will have to specify a device type and the input and output data. The available device types are as follows:

PLA Active High

This is a PLA device with all Active High outputs. This means that the output will be 0 unless the input state matches one of the terms you enter.

PLA Active Low

This is a PLA device with all Active Low outputs. This means that the outputs will be 1 unless the current input combination matches one of the terms you enter.

PROM Bitwise

This is a PROM device with data to be entered as a separate binary string for each output bit. Note that PROM Bitwise and PROM Wordwise give the same device, but data is entered in a different fashion. It is possible to switch between the two and view the same data in two different ways without affecting the data already entered.

PROM Wordwise

This is a PROM device with data entered as one hexadecimal word for each input combination.

You can now proceed to enter data specific to each of the inputs and outputs.

Specify Inputs

Pressing this button will cause the following data-specification dialog box to appear. Note that it is necessary to enter data into this box only if you wish to change the input pin labels in the symbol or the default pin numbers. If no default pin numbers are specified, each newly placed device will appear without pin numbers when it is created. These can be added later if desired using the pin-numbering technique discussed elsewhere in this manual.

```
 ┌─────────────────────────────────────────────────┐
 │  Input Bit Number      [ 0 ]  ( Next )          │
 │                                      ( Cancel )  │
 │  Input Pin Label    [ 0        ]                 │
 │                                                  │
 │  Default Pin Number    [        ]    [  OK  ]    │
 └─────────────────────────────────────────────────┘
```

Specify Outputs

Pressing this button will cause the output data-specification dialog box to appear. This dialog box can be used to enter the actual device data in a variety of formats, so a more detailed discussion follows.

Entering PLA Data

If you have selected a PLA Active High or PLA Active Low device type, the Specify Outputs dialog box will appear with an empty data box, as shown:

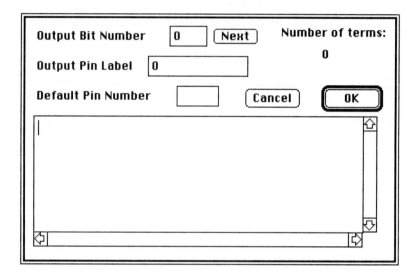

In this box, the OK button must be clicked explicitly, since ⟨←Enter⟩ is used while entering data.

NOTE: Enter characters have significance in delimiting input terms in PLA data. See below.

The text entry cursor will initially be positioned in the Output Bit Number box and can be moved either by clicking in the desired box or pressing ⟨Tab⟩. When you are entering data into the data window, pressing ⟨Tab⟩ will switch you to the next output bit.

NOTE: The number of inputs and outputs cannot be changed once data is entered, because this would invalidate existing data.

A PLA is defined by listing the input combinations that will produce a high (Active High) or low (Active Low) output. Therefore, the data entered for each output bit consists of zero or more input combinations (called terms), typed one per line. Each term gives the state required for each input bit in order to activate the output. The number of characters per line in the data box must be *exactly* equal to the number of input bits. Input bits are given left-to-right from most significant to least, and may have the values 0, 1, or X (Don't Care). Note that X has a different significance here than when used as an output. Specifying X in a term means that the value of the corresponding input bit is ignored. For example, the term 01X would be active for inputs 010 or 011. Up to 64 input terms can be given per output bit, and the output will be active if *any one* of the terms matches the actual inputs. If no terms are listed, the output will never be active. If the term XXX is given, the output will always be active.

The following truth table produces 1 (Active High) outputs for input combinations 001, 011, and 100. This list can be reduced to 0X1 and 100 using standard Boolean algebraic techniques. Exactly the same logic function could be produced by specifying Active Low terms 000, 010, 101, 110, and 111. This list can be reduced to 0X0, 110, and 1X1.

A	B	C	OUT
0	0	0	0
0	0	1	1
0	1	0	0
0	1	1	1
1	0	0	1
1	0	1	0
1	1	0	0
1	1	1	0

Assuming the Active High polarity is chosen, the Specify Outputs dialog box would appear as follows after the reduced term list determined above was entered:

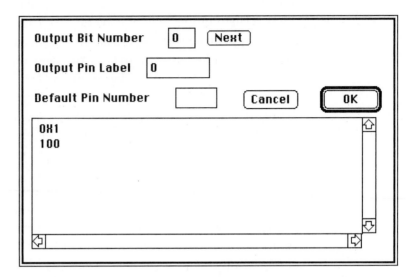

As mentioned above, the same logical results will be obtained by using the basic product term list for this function 001, 011, and 100 or the reduced list 0X1 and 100. Some efficiency and memory usage improvement will be obtained by using the minimized list, because LogicWorks must run sequentially down the list each time any input changes value.

Entering PROM Data

To create a PROM type, you must enter the desired output value for each possible input combination, given in order, starting with 000...0 to 111...1. *Exactly* the right number of characters must be given or you will be told that an error has occurred. Line breaks may be entered as desired by pressing ⏎Enter. Line breaks have no data significance. The number of input combinations is equal to 2^N where N is the number of inputs, or:

Number of inputs	Number of entries
1	2
2	4
3	8
4	16
5	32
6	64
7	128
8	256
9	512
10	1,024
11	2,048
12	4,096

Output values can be any of the following:

0, 1, X (Don't Know), Z (High Impedance)

When the Specify Outputs dialog box first appears, the PROM data will be set to all Xs, as in the following 3-input case using Bitwise entry mode:

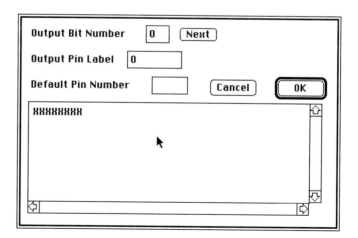

For example, to enter the following truth table (representing a 3-input exclusive OR):

A	B	C	OUT
0	0	0	0
0	0	1	1
0	1	0	1
0	1	1	0
1	0	0	1
1	0	1	0
1	1	0	0
1	1	1	1

the Xs in the data box should be changed to the sequence 01101001, as follows:

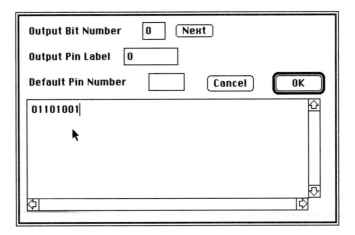

To illustrate Wordwise entry mode, suppose we wish to create a 4-bit incrementer circuit: OUT = IN + 1. This can be done by the following procedure:

■ Select New PROM or PLA.

■ Enter a type name and press Tab.

■ Enter a default delay and press Tab.

■ Set Number of Inputs to 4, press Tab.

■ Set Number of Outputs to 4, press Tab.

■ Click on PROM Wordwise.

■ Click on Specify Outputs. The following dialog box appears:

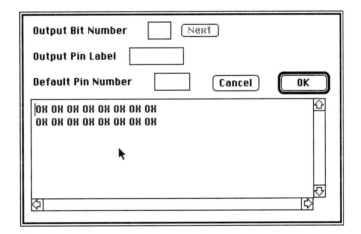

Note that two hex digits appear for each input address and that a digit is set to X if any of the output bits making up that digit are Don't Know or High Impedance. It is not possible to set individual output bits to Don't Know or High Impedance values using Wordwise entry. If the PROM has more than 8 outputs, four hex digits will appear for each input address.

To produce our incrementer, we enter the following data (blanks and returns are optional, but *exactly* the right number of digits must appear):

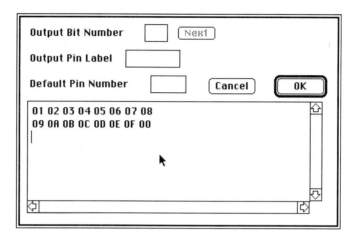

It is possible to switch to a Bitwise view of the data by clicking on the OK button, selecting PROM Bitwise, and clicking on Specify Outputs again. In this case, the data for bit 2 would appear as follows:

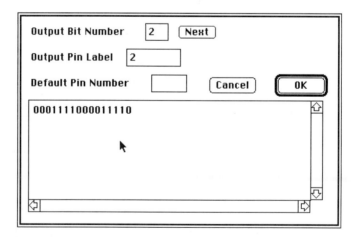

Reading an External PROM/PLA Data File

The Read File option in the PROM/PLA dialog box allows you to read data from an external file into a device definition. This allows devices to be defined using an external logic minimization package. Although it is possible to create one of these files manually using a text editor, we do not recommend it because the formats are complex and any errors may produce unpredictable results.

Data File Formats

The PLA and PROM data files are formatted text files with various text and numeric data fields. For the adventurous, these formats are described in an Appendix to this manual. The PROM data format incorporates the Intel MDS hexadecimal format that is widely used to transfer binary data between machines. This may allow you to use data created by assemblers or other packages to create LogicWorks PROMs.

Creating a New Device from File Data

All the information required to create a PROM or PLA device is contained in the external file, so it is not necessary to enter any information manually. To create a new device using data in a disk file, do the following:

- Click on the Read File button. A standard file box will appear, containing the names of any text files in the current folder with names ending in ".PLA" for PLAs, or ".HEX" for PROMs.

- Select the file containing the device data.

- When the file is read, the type name and other information read from the file will be visible in the PROM/PLA dialog box. The device data can now be edited if desired, or you can simply click on the OK button.

If any file errors were detected, the device data may be in an indeterminate state, and we don't recommend using the device. More information on file errors is given below.

Loading Data into an Existing Device

You can load data into an existing device by selecting the device type for editing (by using the Edit Internals command) and then proceeding exactly as above. Because the data must fit into an existing device, a number of restrictions apply:

- In a PROM device, the number of inputs and outputs in the file must exactly match the existing definition. The number of data words in the file must be exactly correct for the number of inputs and outputs.

- In a PLA device, the number of inputs and outputs must be less than or equal to the number already set. If either number is less than the existing one, the device symbol is not changed, but some of the pins will be nonfunctional.

- For either type of device, pins are associated by pin number, if pin numbers are specified in the file, or by bit number if no pin numbers are given. For example, if a given output is assigned to pin 13 in the file, LogicWorks looks for an output with a default pin number of 13 in the existing device. If none is found, an error message results.

File Errors

If any error is detected in reading the data file, a message is displayed. The following problems will result in the file read being aborted:

- A pin-number assignment specified in the file was not found in the existing device.

- The number of inputs or outputs in the file is greater than the existing device.

- An input or output bit number was used that was not defined in an INPUT or OUTPUT line.

- An incorrect number of data words was in the PROM file.

- An incorrect number of bits was in a TERM line.

Using the PLA or PROM Device

When the desired data has been entered for all output bits, click on the OK button. A new box will appear, allowing you to select an existing library or create a new library in which to place the new type entry. You can now select this device type and create as many incarnations of it as needed, exactly as if it were a standard type. When you save your circuit in a file, the type definitions will be saved with it.

PROM/PLA Symbols

A standard rectangular symbol is created automatically for your PROM or PLA type with the inputs on the left, most significant at the top, and outputs on the right. If you haven't changed the default pin-label or pin-number settings, the symbol will contain simple bit numbers and no pin numbers, as in the examples below.

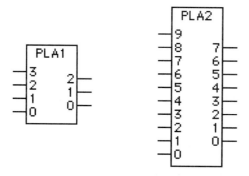

If you wish to create your own symbol, you can save the device in a circuit and use the device library facility to assign that circuit to a symbol of your creation. See Chapter 12, The Device Editor, for more information on this procedure.

Effect of Unknown Inputs on a PROM or PLA

When one of the input lines to a PLA or PROM device is in an unknown state (Don't Know, Conflict, or High Impedance), LogicWorks follows certain rules to determine what effect this value will have on the output lines.

In a PROM device, any unknown input causes all the outputs to become unknown. In some cases, this may not be a correct interpretation, since the value of a given output may be independent of the unknown input with a certain input combination. The only way of determining this, however, is to try all possible combinations of unknown inputs to see if the output changes. Because this is impractical from a time-efficiency point of view, we have taken the easy way out.

In a PLA device, it is more practical to correctly evaluate unknown inputs. Each AND term in the term list is evaluated and the output from that term is determined to be one of the following:

0   Input values do not match term.

1   Input values match term and unknowns occur only in Don't Care positions.

X   Input values match term except where unknowns occur.

If any term evaluates to 1, the output will be active (high or low), because 1 ORed with anything produces a 1. If no term produces a 1 and some term produces an X, the output is set to X.

Editing the PROM or PLA Device Data

You can reenter the data dialog box for a PROM or PLA device by selecting it (clicking on it) and choosing Edit Internals from the Options menu. This will also work for PLAs inside macros so long as the "Allow reload" switch was turned on when the PLA was created. You cannot change the number of inputs or outputs, because this would affect device symbols already placed in the circuit, but the data can be modified as desired by editing the text in the data box of the Specify Outputs dialog box.

PROM/PLA Examples

1-Bit Full Adder

The following truth table gives the logic for a 1-bit adder circuit that accepts two 1-bit input values plus a carry from the previous bit and produces a sum bit and a carry-out to the next stage. This function can be easily implemented using either the PROM or PLA form, although the PROM type is easier to enter for a small number of inputs because the data can be read directly from the truth table.

The required device will have 3 inputs and 2 outputs, which we will assign as follows:

Carry In	Input bit 0 (least significant)
B	Input bit 1
A	Input bit 2
Sum	Output bit 0
Carry Out	Output bit 1

Inputs			Outputs	
A	B	Carry In	Carry Out	Sum
0	0	0	0	0
0	0	1	0	1
0	1	0	0	1
0	1	1	1	0
1	0	0	0	1
1	0	1	1	0
1	1	0	1	0
1	1	1	1	1

Select the command New PROM or PLA from the Options menu. In the first dialog box, enter the name PROMADDER (or any other that suits you), select the PROM button, and choose Specify.

To create the PROM type:

- ■ Select the command New PROM or PLA from the Options menu.

- ■ In the Type Name box, enter the name PROMADDER (or any other that suits you).

- ■ Click in the Inputs box and type 3.

- ■ Click in the Outputs box and type 2.

- ■ Select the PROM Bitwise button.

- ■ Click on the Specify Outputs button.

To enter the PROM form data:

- ■ Click in the data box and replace the default value XXXXXXXX that appears with 01101001 for output bit 0 (read directly from the truth table column for Sum).

- ■ Click on the Next button for output bit 1 and enter 00010111 (for Carry Out) in the data box.

- ■ Click on OK.

- ■ Click on OK in the initial dialog box.

- ■ Select the library in which to place the new type definition or create a new library.

The selected library will appear in the parts window, containing the entry PROMADDER (or whatever you entered). Select this entry and place a device where desired in the circuit window. The default symbol created for you numbers the input and output bits from least significant to most significant, so the equivalent adder symbol would be as follows:

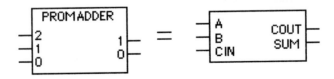

Address Decoder PLA

Suppose we are designing a small microprocessor system and need a device that will examine the address lines coming from the processor and select appropriate RAM, EPROM, or I/O devices, as follows:

Bit	Addresses	Device	Input Pattern
0	F000 - FFFF	EPROM	1111XXXXXXXX
1	0000 - 7FFF	RAM	0XXXXXXXXXXX
2	8000 - 800F	Video	100000000000
3	8010 - 801F	Serial	100000000001
4	8020 - 802F	Parallel	100000000010
5	8030 - 803F	Sound	100000000011

The Input Pattern shown above represents the states of the 12 most significant address lines emerging from the processor, A4 to A15. This is an ideal PLA application, because the patterns are easily determined and the number of inputs makes the PROM form impractical.

To create this device type:

■ Select command New PROM or PLA from the Options menu.

■ In the Type Name box, enter the name SYSDECODE (or any other name) and press [Tab ⇥].

■ Enter a new Default Delay value, if desired, or just press [Tab ⇥].

■ Enter the number 12 in the Inputs box and press [Tab ⇥].

■ Enter the number 6 in the outputs box and press [Tab ⇥].

■ Select the "PLA Active Low" button.

■ Click on the Specify Outputs button.

To enter the PLA data:

■ Click in the data box and enter 1111XXXXXXXX for output bit 0 (read directly from the pattern above).

■ Click on the Next button to select output bit 1 and enter 0XXXXXXXXXXX in the data box.

■ Proceed and enter the patterns for bits 2 to 5.

■ Click on OK. You will return to the initial PROM/PLA dialog box.

■ Click on OK in this box.

■ Select the library in which to place the new type, or create a new library.

The selected library will appear in the parts window, containing the entry SYSDECODE (or whatever you entered). Select this entry and place it where desired in the circuit window. The default symbol created for you numbers the input and output bits from least significant to most significant.

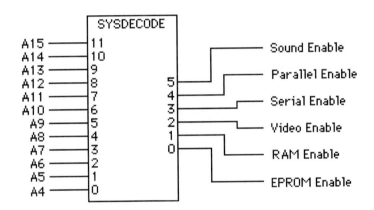

10
Primitive Devices

This chapter provides information on the "primitive" or built-in device types in LogicWorks. These types are intended primarily for use in creating model circuits for higher-level macro devices. Because their simulation functions are hard-coded, they occupy much less memory space than macro devices and simulate more efficiently.

The following table lists the available primitives and their functions.

Device Type	74LS Equivalent	Description
NOT	04	Inverter
AND-2	08	2-input AND gate
AND-3	11	3-input AND gate
AND-4	21	4-input AND gate
AND-5	—	5-input AND gate
NAND-2	00	2-input NAND gate
NAND-3	10	3-input NAND gate
NAND-4	20	4-input NAND gate
NAND-5	—	5-input NAND gate
NAND-8	30	8-input NAND gate
OR-2	32	2-input OR gate
OR-3	—	3-input OR gate
OR-4	—	4-input OR gate
OR-5	—	5-input OR gate
NOR-2	02	2-input NOR gate
NOR-3	27	3-input NOR gate
NOR-4	25 *	4-input NOR gate

* Approximate equivalence

Device Type	74LS Equivalent	Description
NOR-5	260 *	5-input NOR gate
XOR-2	86	2-input XOR gate
XNOR-2	266	2-input XNOR gate
O.C.Buffer	07	Non-inverting open-collector buffer
O.C.NAND	03	Open-collector 2-input NAND
X-Gate	—	Transmission gate
T.S.Buffer-1	125	Non-inverting three-state buffer with inverted enable
T.S.Buffer-4	367 *	Non-inverting quad three-state buffer with common inverted enable
Pullup A	—	Pullup resistor (diamond symbol)
Pullup B	—	Pullup resistor (resistor symbol)
Resistor	—	2-pin resistor
Buffer-1	—	Non-inverting single buffer
Multiplexer	151 *	8-to-1 multiplexer
Decoder	138 *	3-to-8 line decoder
Adder-4	83	4-bit adder with carry in and out
D Flip Flop	74	D-type flip-flop
D Flip Flop ni	—	D-type flip-flop (non-inv S & R)
JK Flip Flop	76	JK flip-flop
JK Flip Flop ni	—	JK flip-flop (non-inv S & R)
Register-8	374 *	8-bit register with clear
Counter-4	191 *	4-bit synchronous counter
Shift Reg-4	177 *	4-bit shift register
One-Shot	123 *	Retriggerable one-shot
Clock Osc	624 *	Clock oscillator
Binary Switch	—	Debounced toggle switch
SPST Switch	—	Open/closed single-pole switch
SPDT Switch	—	Double throw switch
SPDT Pushbutton	—	Momentary switch
Logic Probe	—	Signal-level display
Hex Keyboard	—	Hexadecimal input device
Hex Display	—	Hexadecimal digit display
ASCII Display	—	Single-character ASCII display
Page Connector	—	Page connector for signals

* Approximate equivalence

The Gates Library

The Gates library contains the primitive gates with a built-in simulation function. The NOT, AND, NAND, OR, NOR, and XOR devices behave according to the appropriate truth tables for such devices. Any gate input which is in the Don't Know, High Impedance, or Conflict state is treated as a Don't Know. A gate with a Don't Know input will not necessarily produce a Don't Know output. For example, if one input of an AND gate is low, the output will be low, regardless of the state of the other input, as in the following truth table:

A	B	OUT
0	0	0
0	1	0
0	X	0
1	0	0
1	1	1
1	X	X
X	0	0
X	1	X
X	X	X

O.C.NAND-2

2-input NAND gate with open-collector output.

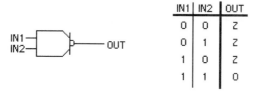

IN1	IN2	OUT
0	0	Z
0	1	Z
1	0	Z
1	1	0

Transmission Gate

The transmission gate (X-Gate) device behaves as an electrically controlled SPST switch. When the control input is high, any level change occurring on one signal pin will be passed through to the other. Because it has no drive capability of its own, it will behave differently from a typical logic device when a high-impedance or low drive-level signal is applied to its signal inputs. Most other primitives, such as gates, interpret any applied input as either High, Low, or Don't Know. The transmission gate, on the other hand, will pass through exactly the drive level found on its opposite pin. Thus, a high-impedance level on one pin will be transmitted as a high-impedance level on the other pin. Note that the simulation of this device may produce unpredictable results in extreme cases, such as an unbroken ring of transmission gates.

The Generic Library

The Generic library contains the non-gate primitive devices having a built-in simulation function in LogicWorks. Other, more complex macro devices can be built up from these devices. It is most efficient to use a primitive device whenever possible in producing simulation models for other devices, because they have the least overhead in terms of memory usage and execution time.

T.S.Buffer-1

The three-state buffer has two inputs, a data input and an active-low enable input. If the enable input is high, the output is in a High Impedance state, which may be modified by other devices connected to the same signal line. If the enable input is low, the output will follow the data input if it is low or high, or produce a Don't Know level otherwise.

ENABLE	DATA	OUT
0	0	0
0	1	1
1	0	Z
1	1	Z

T.S.Buffer-4

This device consists of 4 three-state buffers in a single package with all the enable inputs connected to a common pin.

Buffer-1

This device is a single, non-inverting buffer, that is, a non-inverting inverter. Its primary simulation function is to insert a delay in a signal path without affecting the logic of the system.

O.C.Buffer

The open-collector buffer produces a low output level when its input is low, and a high-impedance output when its input is high. The output signal may take on some other level depending on what other device outputs are connected to it. For example, if a pullup resistor is present, the output will go high when the input is high. Refer to the following diagram:

IN	OUT
0	0
1	Z

IN	OUT
0	0
1	1

IN1	IN2	OUT
0	0	0
0	1	0
1	0	0
1	1	1

Pullup Resistors

The Pullup Resistor is a device which forces a high-impedance signal to a high level, but has no effect on any other level. This can be used in conjunction with the open-collector or three-state buffers to implement wired-AND and other similar logic functions or to tie unused inputs to a high level. Pullup A uses a small diamond symbol which is more convenient on a group of adjacent lines. Pullup B uses a conventional resistor symbol but otherwise behaves identically.

Resistor

The Resistor device simulates the effects of a resistor in a digital circuit. It is more general than the Pullup Resistor device and can be used as a pullup, pulldown, or series resistor. Whenever a signal-level change occurs on either pin of the resistor, the device converts that level into a resistive drive level (see Chapter 8, Simulation, for more information on drive levels). A high-impedance drive on one end is transmitted as a high-impedance output to the other end. Note that LogicWorks does not simulate analog properties of devices, so the resistor device does not have a resistance value in the analog sense and will not interact with capacitor symbols placed on the same line. The effect of resistance on line delay can be simulated by setting the delay of the resistor device.

Multiplexer

This is a device that selects one of 8 data inputs and routes it to a single output line. It obeys the following function table in which X = Don't Care.

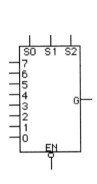

EN	S2	S1	S0	7	6	5	4	3	2	1	0	G
0	0	0	0	X	X	X	X	X	X	X	0	0
0	0	0	0	X	X	X	X	X	X	X	1	1
0	0	0	1	X	X	X	X	X	X	0	X	0
0	0	0	1	X	X	X	X	X	X	1	X	1
0	0	1	0	X	X	X	X	X	0	X	X	0
0	0	1	0	X	X	X	X	X	1	X	X	1
0	0	1	1	X	X	X	X	0	X	X	X	0
0	0	1	1	X	X	X	X	1	X	X	X	1
0	1	0	0	X	X	X	0	X	X	X	X	0
0	1	0	0	X	X	X	1	X	X	X	X	1
0	1	0	1	X	X	0	X	X	X	X	X	0
0	1	0	1	X	X	1	X	X	X	X	X	1
0	1	1	0	X	0	X	X	X	X	X	X	0
0	1	1	0	X	1	X	X	X	X	X	X	1
0	1	1	1	0	X	X	X	X	X	X	X	0
0	1	1	1	1	X	X	X	X	X	X	X	1
1	X	X	X	X	X	X	X	X	X	X	X	1

Decoder

The Decoder activates one of 8 outputs, depending on 3 select inputs, as follows (X = Don't Care):

EN	S2	S1	S0	7	6	5	4	3	2	1	0
0	0	0	0	1	1	1	1	1	1	1	0
0	0	0	1	1	1	1	1	1	1	0	1
0	0	1	0	1	1	1	1	1	0	1	1
0	0	1	1	1	1	1	1	0	1	1	1
0	1	0	0	1	1	1	0	1	1	1	1
0	1	0	1	1	1	0	1	1	1	1	1
0	1	1	0	1	0	1	1	1	1	1	1
0	1	1	1	0	1	1	1	1	1	1	1
1	X	X	X	1	1	1	1	1	1	1	1

Adder

The 4-bit Adder device accepts two 4-bit input arguments and a 1-bit carry, and outputs their 4-bit sum plus a 1-bit carry out. Multiple adders can be connected together by feeding the carry out from each stage to the carry in of the next, more significant stage. The carry in to the least significant stage should be set to 0.

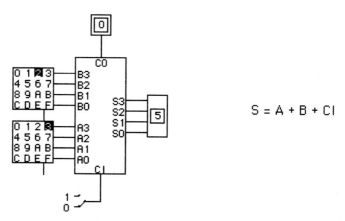

$$S = A + B + CI$$

D Flip Flop

The D-type flip-flop is positive-edge triggered and obeys the following function table, where * means "Don't Care":

S	R	D	Clock	Q	Q/
0	0	*	*	1	1
0	1	*	*	1	0
1	0	*	*	0	1
1	1	0	Rises	0	1
1	1	1	Rises	1	0

In addition to the entries in the table, the simulator will distinguish a number of cases where the outputs will be known, despite unknown inputs. For example, if R = 1, C = 0, D = 0, Q is currently high, and S is unknown, Q will remain high.

Note that when a flip-flop is first created, it is in an unknown state and must be correctly initialized before it will produce predictable outputs. This can be done by adding circuitry to force an explicit reset or by using the Clear Unknowns command from the Options menu.

D Flip Flop ni

The D Flip Flop ni is identical to the standard D Flip Flop except that the polarity of the Set and Reset inputs is reversed. That is, a high value on the Set input will set the device.

JK Flip Flop

The JK-type flip-flop is negative-edge triggered and obeys the following function table, where * means "Don't Care":

S	R	J	K	Clock	Old Q	New Q
0	0	*	*	*	*	1
0	1	*	*	*	*	1
1	0	*	*	*	*	0
1	1	0	0	falls	0	0
1	1	0	0	falls	1	1
1	1	0	1	falls	*	0
1	1	1	0	falls	*	1
1	1	1	1	falls	0	1
1	1	1	1	falls	1	0

If any inputs are in an unknown state, the simulator will determine the output state where possible or else set it to Don't Know.

Note that when a flip-flop is first created, it is in an unknown state and must be correctly initialized before it will produce predictable outputs. This can be done by adding circuitry to force an explicit reset or by using the Clear Unknowns command from the Options menu.

JK Flip Flop ni

The JK Flip Flop ni is identical to the standard JK Flip Flop except that the polarity of the Set and Reset inputs is reversed. That is, a high value on the Set input will set the device.

Register-8

This device implements an 8-bit, positive-edge–triggered register with common clock and active-high clear inputs.

Counter

This device implements a 4-bit, presettable, synchronous, positive-edge–triggered counter. The following timing diagram shows a typical count cycle. Note that the CO (Carry Out) output goes low when the count reaches 15_{10} and rises again on the next count. This can be used to cascade multiple counters together, as shown. The CLR input clears the counter asynchronously (that is, regardless of the state of the clock). The Count/Load input, when low, causes the data from the 4 inputs to be passed to the outputs on the rising edge of the next clock.

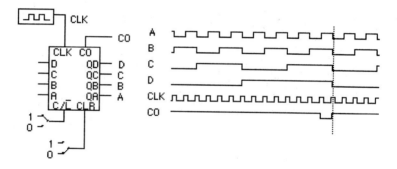

Cascading Multiple Counters

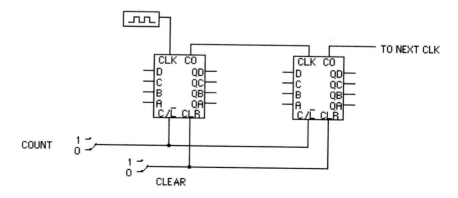

Shift Reg

The Shift Register is a 4-bit, positive-edge–triggered device with serial or parallel load. When the Shift/Load input is low, data from the 4 parallel data input lines is transferred to the outputs on the rising edge of the next clock. When Shift/Load is high, the next rising clock edge causes the value at the Shift In (SI) input becomes the new value for output A, A shifts to B, B to C, C to D, and the old value at D is lost. An example shift sequence follows:

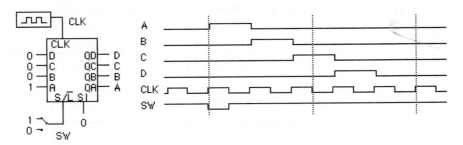

Clock Osc

The Clock Oscillator is used to generate a repeating signal to activate other devices. When it is first created, the clock output pin will be low; then, after a delay time called the "low time," it will change to the high state. After a further delay called the "high time," the signal will revert to low, and the cycle will repeat. The low and high times are initially set to 10, but can be modified using Set Params from the Options menu. Any number of clocks may exist at once with independent delay times. If you want to create several clocks with related output frequencies and synchronized transitions, this can be done by pausing the simulation (using Pause from the Options menu) and then creating and setting the values for all desired clocks. When you select Continue, the initial transition for those devices will occur at the same time and all subsequent transitions will be relative to that time.

Setting Clock Values

To set the high and low times for a clock, either:

■ Select the device (by setting the cursor to point mode and clicking inside the device symbol), then choose Set Params from the Options menu, or

■ Hold down [Alt] and click on the Clock Osc device.

You will be presented with a dialog box with buttons for increasing or decreasing the high and low values. The minimum for either value is 1 and the maximum is 32,767.

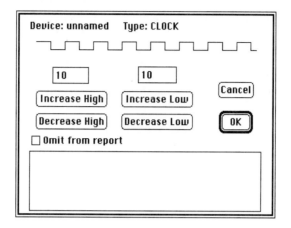

One-Shot

The One-Shot device is used to generate an output pulse of a fixed length when it is triggered by the rising edge of the trigger input. Two parameters can be set for a one-shot: the delay from the rising edge of the input to the start of the output pulse and the duration of the pulse. The delay and duration times are initially set to 1 and 10, respectively, but can be modified using Set Params from the Options menu.

The One-Shot device is retriggerable, meaning that the output pulse will not end until duration time has passed since the last trigger input. Repeating the trigger input can cause the output pulse to be extended indefinitely.

The following circuit shows 2 one-shots hooked together to form an astable multivibrator. In this case, the delay and duration times are set to 5 and 25 for the left-hand device and 5 and 35 for the right-hand device.

Setting One-Shot Values

To set the delay and duration times for a one-shot, either:

■ Select the device (by setting the cursor to point mode and clicking inside the device symbol), then choose Set Params from the Options menu, or

■ Hold down ⟨Alt⟩ and click on the One-Shot device.

The following dialog box appears:

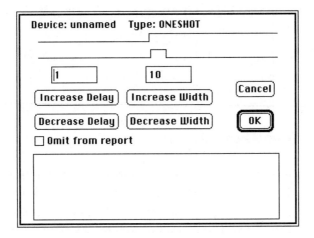

The buttons can be used to increase or decrease the delay and duration values, or you can type numbers directly into the corresponding box. The minimum for either value is 1 and the maximum is 127. The sample input and output waveforms shown in the box are drawn using the current setting for timing resolution.

The I/O Library

Binary Switch

The Binary Switch device provides a means for setting a signal to a low or high level. When a switch is first created, its output is at a low level. Pointing at the switch with the cursor in point mode and clicking the mouse button causes the switch arm to move and the output to change to the opposite state. Any number of device inputs can be driven by a switch output. A switch has no delay characteristic, since it has no inputs.

SPST Switch

The SPST Switch device simulates the actions of a simple open/closed switch in a digital circuit. When a switch is first created, it is open, and both connections present a high-impedance logic level. Clicking on the switch with the cursor in point mode causes the switch arm to close and the switch to conduct. In terms of the digital simulation, this means that whatever logic level is present on each pin is transmitted to the other one.

An SPST switch has a default delay of 0, but this can be set to any value from 0 to 32,767 using the Set Params command. The ⟨⇧Shift⟩ key must be pressed while clicking on the mouse button to select a Switch device.

SPDT Switch

The SPDT Switch device operates in essentially the same manner as the SPST switch described above, except that it always conducts between the single pin on one side and one of the two pins on the other. As with the other two switch types, clicking on it in point mode changes the position of the contact.

Logic Probe

The Logic Probe is a device for displaying the level present on any signal line. When the probe is first created, its input is unconnected and therefore in the High Impedance state, which will be displayed as a Z. When the input pin is connected to another signal, the displayed character will change to reflect the new signal's current state. Any further changes in the signal state will be shown on the probe. Possible displayed values are 0 (low), 1 (high), X (Don't Know), Z (High Impedance), or C (Conflict).

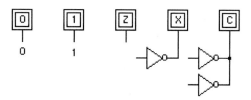

Hex Keyboard

The Hex Keyboard device outputs the binary equivalent of a hexadecimal digit on four binary lines. A "key" is pressed by positioning the tip of the arrow cursor in the desired key number and clicking the mouse button. The binary data on the output lines will change to reflect the new value and remain until the next key is pressed. On a fifth line, it outputs a signal which goes high momentarily and then low again when a key is pressed.

Hex Display

The Hex Display device shows the hexadecimal equivalent of its four binary inputs. If any of the inputs is Unknown, High Impedance, or Conflict, an X will be displayed.

User-Definable Primitives

LogicWorks supports several types of primitive devices that have user-definable characteristics. Since a wide variety of configurations are possible, these types are not included in external libraries but are generated automatically according to user-specified options.

The creation of PROM and PLA devices is covered in Chapter 9, PROM and PLA Devices.

Creating RAM Devices

The RAM primitive provides a means for creating static RAM devices with full simulation in a variety of configurations. Selecting the New RAM command from the Options menu will display the following dialog box:

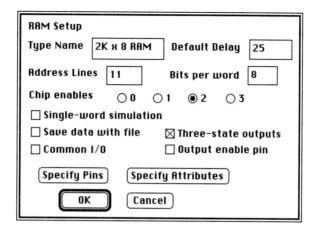

Type Name

This is the name that will be used to reference the device in the library menu.

Address Lines

This is the number of address inputs to the device and must be between 1 and 24. The number of words of memory will be 2^N where N is the number of address lines. If you attempt to create a device with full simulation that is larger than the amount of memory available, you will get an error message.

Bits per Word

This is the number of data bits per memory word and must be between 1 and 32.

Default Delay

This is the default delay, from 0 to 32,767, for this device type. This can be changed for individual incarnations of the device using Set Params.

Control Pin Selections

The number of "Output enable" and "Chip enable" pins can be set to suit the requirements of the application. All these inputs are active-low.

Save Data with File

If this is checked, the data stored in the RAM will be stored in the data file; otherwise, the RAM will be reinitialized each time the file is read.

Single-Word Simulation

If this is checked, only a single word of simulation memory will be allocated. This makes it possible to simulate RAMs larger than the available memory when only access time is important and the actual stored data is not required.

Three-State Outputs

If this is checked, the data outputs will be the three-state type; otherwise they will not be disabled when the chip is disabled.

Common I/O

When this is checked, the data in and out pins for each bit will be combined.

You can accept the device settings as displayed and close the RAM dialog box by clicking on the OK button or pressing [←Enter]. Clicking on the Cancel button discards any changes made. You will then be prompted to select an open library or create a new library in which to place the new device type.

The newly created device type will appear as an entry in the selected library in the parts window. It can be selected from there and placed in the schematic just like any other device type or, if desired, modified using the DevEditor module.

A symbol for the selected RAM type is generated automatically based on the selected options.

11

Menu Reference

The MCP Menu

The MCP menu offers some environment options. The About LogicWorks option provides information about the program and its creator. There are also three desk accessories that can be used during a LogicWorks session: a calculator, a clock, and a control panel.

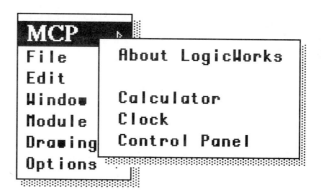

The control panel allows hardware and environment parameters to be selected. The printer type and port can be set, and keyboard and mouse options determined. The screen background and screen saver can be chosen.

The File Menu

The **File menu** contains the commands required for creating new files, accessing existing circuit files on disk, saving files, accessing device libraries, and printing.

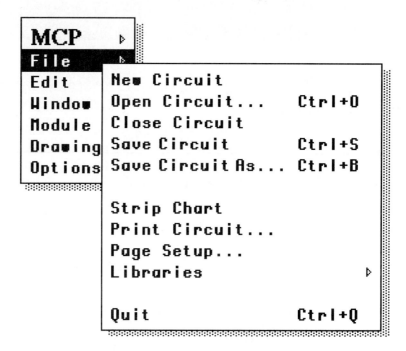

Creating a New Circuit

New Circuit opens a new, empty circuit window on the screen. The circuit will use the current printer Page Setup for its sheet size. More information on these settings is provided under the Sheet Size and Display Options commands. New Circuit has no effect on any files on your disk.

Reading In an Existing Circuit File

Open Circuit creates a new circuit window and allows you to select a circuit file from your disk to be read into it. A dialog box is displayed, showing the names of all the circuit files on the current disk. If there are more files on the disk than can be listed in the box, a scroll bar can be used to scan through the list. To search a different drive for files, click on the Drive button. Once the name of the file you want is displayed in the window, open it by clicking on the name once and then clicking on the Open button, or simply by double-clicking on the name.

When you open a file, the circuit data is read into memory in its entirety and no more access to the disk file is required. LogicWorks will let you open multiple copies of the same file and makes no attempt to restrict you from writing any of them back to the same file. If you do this, it is up to you to keep track of which windows have been updated and what file you want to save them into.

If the circuit was saved using the current version of LogicWorks, the window size and position, display scale, and timing settings will be set to the values they were when the circuit was saved.

Closing the Current File

Close Circuit closes the circuit and timing windows and removes all data from memory. If any changes have been made to your circuit since the last Open or Save, you will be asked if you wish to save those changes. The same effect is achieved by clicking the Go-Away box in the upper-left corner of the circuit window. The Close menu item is disabled if there is no circuit information in memory.

Saving Your Circuit

Save Circuit and **Save Circuit As** save the current drawing in a circuit file. Save Circuit saves the circuit back into the file that was most recently opened. It will be disabled if no file has been opened. If you select Save Circuit As, a dialog box will be displayed, requesting the name the new file. The default name will be the current title of the circuit window (the name of the most recently opened or saved file), or "Circuit" if the file has not been previously saved. As in Open Circuit, you can save your file to a disk on a different drive using the Disk button. Save Circuit As is disabled if there is no current circuit information.

Print a Timing Strip Chart

The **Strip Chart** command causes all subsequent traces drawn on the timing diagram to be echoed on the printer. The current page setup for the circuit is used to select paper type, orientation, and so on.

Timing information is saved internally until a complete page is available, and then that page is printed. This process is repeated indefinitely until Strip Chart is selected again, or Ctrl-. (period) is typed while a page print is in progress.

Strip Chart mode will print only as many signals as will fit on the page. There are no provisions in this version of LogicWorks for multipanel strip charts.

Printing

The **Print** command appears as either Print Circuit or Print Timing, depending on which window is currently active. A window is activated by clicking anywhere in it.

Print Circuit allows you to print all or part of your circuit diagram. If the diagram will not fit on a single page, it will be broken into as many parts as are needed, based on the paper size specified in Page Setup. You can preview the page breaks by using the Show Page Breaks option of the Display Options command. So you can specify a range to print, pages are numbered from left to right and top to bottom. Page numbers do not appear in the printed output.

Print Timing allows you to print timing information. The current version of LogicWorks has the following restrictions:

▨ Only one page can be printed at a time. Any timing traces that run off the bottom of the page cannot be printed. Any reduction options available with your printer, however, can be used to squeeze more onto the page.

▨ Timing information is discarded as it scrolls off the left edge of the timing window. Therefore, only information in the currently displayed time range can be printed. (This can be overcome using the Strip Chart command.)

The current timing resolution and reference-line settings in effect for this circuit are used in printing timing information.

Page Setup

The **Page Setup** dialog box allows you to choose the size of printer paper you wish to use. Once chosen, this information will be stored with your circuit file and affects the page outlines shown when using the Show Page Outlines option of the Display Options command.

Accessing Device Libraries

Menu commands for opening, closing, and accessing libraries are located in the **Libraries menu**. See Chapter 14, The Parts Window, for more information on libraries.

Exiting LogicWorks

Select the **Quit** command to get out of LogicWorks and go back to DOS. If you have made circuit changes since the last Save, Open, or New, a dialog box will appear asking whether you wish to save those changes.

The Edit Menu

The **Edit menu** contains the commands for editing circuit objects and setting the cursor mode. LogicWorks uses an internal clipboard for editing operations. This clipboard cannot be accessed from outside of LogicWorks.

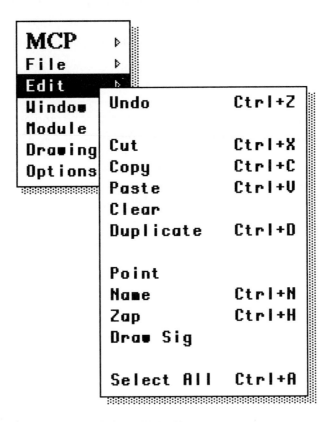

Undo

The **Undo** command is not available for circuit editing. This item will be enabled only when the timing window, DevEditor, or a desk accessory is active.

Using the Clipboard

The LogicWorks clipboard commands Cut, Copy, and Paste can be used to move or copy circuit fragments and graphical and text information within a single circuit window or between multiple windows.

Editing the Timing Window

The clipboard commands Cut, Copy, Paste, Clear, and Duplicate can be used to edit waveforms displayed in the timing window. This topic is covered in Chapter 8, Simulation.

Editing the Circuit Window

Cut and Copy work on the currently selected group of devices and signals and will be disabled if no devices or signals are selected. See "Selecting Circuit Objects" in Chapter 5, Creating the Schematic, for information on selecting items. When items are copied onto the clipboard, their names are copied with them, which may result in duplicate names. If duplicate signal names are pasted back into the circuit page they were copied from, logical connections will be made between the like-named segments.

Cut

Cut removes the currently selected objects from the circuit and transfers them to the clipboard. It is equivalent to selecting Copy, then Clear. Cut will be disabled if no devices or signals are selected.

Copy

Copy places the currently selected objects onto the clipboard without removing them from the drawing. This can be used to duplicate a circuit group or to copy it from one file to another. See the notes on clipboard data above. Copy will be disabled if no device or group is currently selected.

Paste

Paste replaces the cursor with a flickering image in the circuit window of the clipboard contents. The image of the clipboard data can be dragged around and positioned as desired. The item will be made a permanent part of your diagram when the mouse button is pressed.

LogicWorks checks for signal connections only at "loose ends" in the signal lines being pasted, that is, ends of line segments that do not touch devices or other line segments. For example, if the following circuit scrap were pasted, the points marked X would be checked for connection to the existing circuit.

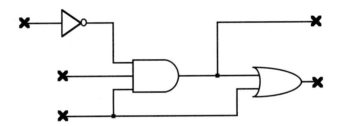

Connection "hit testing" can be disabled by holding down Alt while clicking the mouse button (this also applies to single-device placing). In this case, the circuit scrap is placed, but no connections will be made to adjacent items. This allows the group to be selected again (by double-clicking on any device in the group) and moved without interactions with other objects in the circuit.

Paste will be disabled if there is no information of a recognized type on the clipboard.

Clear

Clear removes the currently selected devices and signals from the circuit after confirming with an OK/Cancel dialog box.

WARNING: This cannot be undone!

Typing ⌫Backspace is equivalent to Clear. This will be disabled if no devices or signals are selected.

Duplicate

Duplicate makes a copy of the selected circuit group that can be dragged and positioned as desired. This is equivalent to selecting Copy and then Paste, except that the selected circuit scrap is not placed on the clipboard for future use. See the notes under Paste, above, on how connections are made when a group is placed in the circuit.

Point

The **Point** command selects the normal operating mode for LogicWorks, indicated by the normal (arrow) cursor. Selecting this command is equivalent to clicking on the pointer icon in the tool palette. The following functions are accessible in point mode:

- Clicking on an input device such as Switch or Keyboard changes its state.

- Clicking on an object selects it for operations using the Edit menu commands. To select an I/O device, or to select multiple objects, hold down ⇧Shift while you click.

- By clicking and dragging near the end of a signal line extends that line in any direction.

- Clicking and dragging a signal line anywhere but near its end changes its perpendicular position.

- Clicking and dragging any other object repositions it.

All of the above functions are described in more detail in Chapter 5, Creating the Schematic.

Shortcuts to Point Mode

Because you will frequently want to return to point mode, two shortcuts are provided:

- Clicking the menu button on the mouse

- Pressing Spacebar

Name

The **Name** command changes the current cursor to name mode and is equivalent to clicking on the pencil icon in the tool palette. In this mode, the following functions are available:

- A name can be associated with a device by clicking and holding on the device in question, dragging the cursor to the desired position for the text, then releasing the button. Type the desired name (up to 15 characters) followed by ⏎Enter.

- A name can be associated with a signal by clicking and holding anywhere along a signal line, then proceeding as for devices above. Signal names differ from device names in that they can appear at multiple locations along the length of the signal line, up to a maximum of 100 positions. Name positions are added by simply repeating the naming procedure as many times as required. If the name at any position is altered, all positions are updated.

- A pin number can be placed on a device pin by clicking on the pin within 5 screen dots of the device. A blinking insertion point will appear, and you will be able to type up to four characters. Press ⏎Enter to complete the pin number.

- Random text not associated with a specific device or signal can be placed anywhere on the diagram by clicking on the diagram away from any device or signal. This text can contain returns or any other characters.

- Any of the above text items can be edited by clicking anywhere in the existing object. The blinking insertion point will appear in the text at the position of the click.

All of the above functions are described in more detail in Chapter 5, Creating the Schematic.

Zap

The **Zap** command changes the current cursor to Zap mode and is equivalent to clicking on the lightning bolt icon in the tool palette. When the tip of this cursor is clicked on any object in a circuit, that object is permanently removed. In the case of signal lines, only the line segment under the cursor is removed. See Chapter 5, Creating the Schematic, for more information on this command and other editing features.

Draw Sig

The **Draw Sig** command is equivalent to clicking on the crosshair icon in the tool palette and places the program in signal-drawing mode. In this mode, you can draw or extend signal lines as follows:

■ Click anywhere along an existing signal line to create a new line starting at that point. When you click again, the lines on the screen become permanent and a new set of lines are drawn starting at that point. A number of line-routing options are selected by pressing Ctrl, Alt, and ⇧Shift while drawing. To terminate signal-drawing mode, press Spacebar or click the menu button.

■ Click anywhere on the diagram while pressing Ctrl to create a new line not attached to any existing signal. This is done to prevent unattached signals from being created accidentally.

For more information on signal-drawing modes, see Chapter 5, Creating the Schematic.

Select All

This command selects and highlights all elements in the current circuit. The entire circuit can then be operated on with the clipboard commands and other commands that work on selected items.

The Window Menu

The **Window menu** is provided as an alternative means of locating any displayed window that may have been hidden by others on the screen. Windows appear in the menu in the order they were created. Select the appropriate window to bring to the foreground.

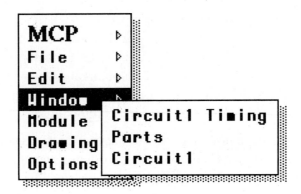

The Module Menu

The **Module menu** is provided to allow access to utility modules. If a given module is already active (that is, has a check mark by its name), selecting it will have the effect of bringing one of its windows to the foreground. If it is inactive, its function will be invoked. In case multiple modules share the same menu commands, the frontmost module is the one whose function is invoked when a shared item is selected.

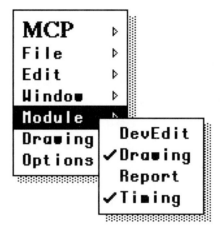

The items Drawing and Timing will always appear in the Module menu. These refer to the drawing and simulation windows of LogicWorks. Because these are always active, the only effect of selecting one of them is to bring its window to the foreground and activate its menu items.

The Drawing Menu

The **Drawing menu** contains commands for positioning and scaling the drawing on the screen and for setting display and printing options.

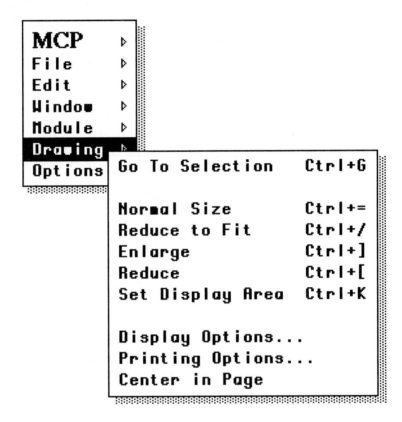

Go To Selection

The **Go To Selection** command causes the circuit position and scaling to be adjusted so that the currently selected items are centered and just fit in the circuit window. The scaling will be set to 100% maximum.

Screen-Scaling Commands

Four commands are provided that control the enlargement or reduction of the circuit diagram on the screen. These commands control screen display only and have no effect on the stored circuit information, printed output, or graphics files. The maximum enlargement allowed is 200% and the minimum is 20% of Normal Size. Due to the integer calculations that are done by LogicWorks, device symbols and text may be displayed rather crudely at scale factors other than 100%. It is best to do most editing at Normal Size to ensure that everything lines up as you expect.

Normal Size

Normal Size sets the screen scale to 100%.

Reduce to Fit

Reduce to Fit sets the scale factor and centers the display so that the entire diagram fits on the screen. If the size of the diagram and the size of the window is such that this would require a scale factor of less than 20%, the scale is set to 20% and the diagram is centered. If the diagram fits completely in the window at 100%, the scale is set to 100% and the diagram is centered.

Enlarge

Enlarge increases the scale factor by about 20%, causing the diagram to appear larger on the screen, up to a maximum of 200% of Normal Size.

Reduce

Reduce decreases the scale factor by about 20%, causing the diagram to appear smaller on the screen, down to a minimum of 20% of Normal Size.

Set Display Area

This command provides an alternative method to select a circuit area for viewing. When you select **Set Display Area**, the cursor changes into a right angle pointing down and to the right.

Zooming In

Clicking and dragging the mouse down and to the right zooms in on the selected area. The point at which you click the mouse button will become the top-left corner of the new viewing area. If you press and hold the button and move to a new position, the point at which you release the button will become approximately the lower-right corner of the displayed area. The circuit position and scaling will be adjusted to display the indicated area.

Zooming Out

Clicking and dragging the mouse up and to the left zooms out to view more of the schematic in the window. The degree of change in the scale factor is determined by how far the mouse is moved. Moving a small distance zooms out by one step (equivalent to using the Reduce command). Moving most of the way across the window is equivalent to doing a Reduce to Fit.

Preventing Return to Pointer

The cursor normally returns immediately to point mode. This can be prevented by holding down [Ctrl] to allow multiple zoom operations.

Display Options

Selecting **Display Options** brings up the following dialog box:

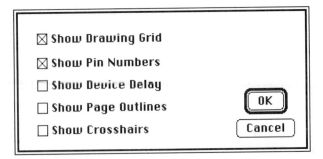

- ■ **Show Drawing Grid** controls the display of visible grid lines in the circuit window. The grid is normally displayed every 50 screen dots.

- ■ **Show Pin Numbers** controls the display of pin numbers that have been added to the circuit. Pin numbers will be shown only if they were explicitly added to the device (see "Name," above), or were part of the macro device when it was created. The primitive devices (in the Gates and Generic libraries) do not have any default pin numbers.

■ **Show Device Delay**, when enabled, causes the current nominal delay time setting for the device to be drawn in each device symbol, as follows:

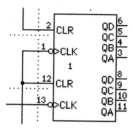

Nothing will be shown for One-Shot, Clock Osc, or input/output devices.

■ **Show Page Outlines**, when enabled, causes a line grid and a page number to appear in the circuit window where the printed sheet breaks will occur. LogicWorks centers the page boundary in the sheet array when it prints it, so these boundaries may move if the circuit is changed in such a way that more sheets are needed.

■ **Show Crosshairs**, when enabled, causes gray crossed lines to appear in the circuit window following the current mouse position. These can be helpful in aligning elements in a circuit diagram.

Printing Options

Selecting the **Printing Options** command displays the same options as the Display Options command above, except for Show Crosshairs. These settings affect how the circuit is drawn for printing.

Center in Page

This item moves the drawing border for the current page so that the circuit objects are centered on the page. This is intended to assist with situations where a diagram has become lopsided due to modifications.

The Options Menu

The **Options menu** contains commands for controlling the simulation, creating PROM and PLA devices, and setting device characteristics.

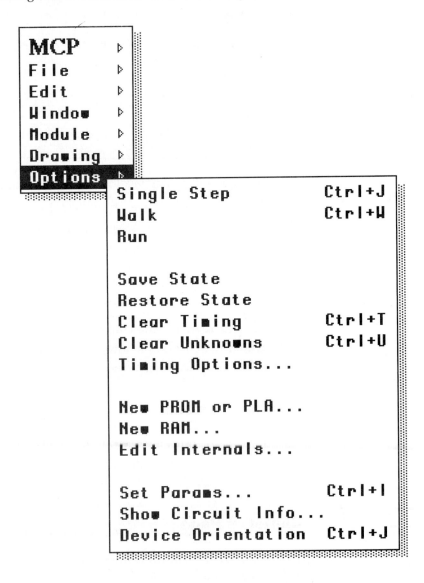

Controlling the Simulation

The Single Step, Walk, and Run menu commands are used to control the simulation speed. The current status is shown in the tool palette at the bottom-left corner of both the circuit and timing windows. Simulation status can be set individually for each open circuit.

Pause/Single Step   Walk   Run

Single Step

The **Single Step** command stops the simulation if it is running or simulates 1 time step if it is not. To perform the single step, the simulator looks at the time value associated with the next signal-change event in the queue, simulates the effect of that and all following events which occur at the same time, then returns to the paused state.

Walk

This command initiates slow stepping through the simulation. It is equivalent to selecting the Single Step command twice per second. The walk mode continues until some other mode is selected or there are no more signal changes in the event queue. Selecting this command is equivalent to clicking on the Walk icon in the tool palette.

Run

This command tells the simulation to proceed as fast as possible.

LogicWorks normally simulates continuously, so that as changes are made to the circuit or to signal inputs, these changes are immediately taken into account in determining device outputs. At times, however, especially when creating large circuits or entering input sequences in the timing diagram, the screen updates and processing delays introduced by the simulation can become a nuisance. At such times it is desirable to pause the simulation by either selecting the Single Step command or clicking on the Pause icon in the tool palette. This causes time to stop progressing in the simulation. Any changes that occur immediately, such as a change in signal level due to a connection being made or a switch being flipped, are reflected on the screen, whereas delayed effects, such as device output changes, are scheduled but will not occur until you allow the simulation to continue.

The timing diagram is not updated when the simulation is paused, so the trace labels and other information may be outdated as you modify the circuit. These will be updated when you continue.

Clearing and Rerunning the Simulation

Save State and Restore State

The **Save State** and **Restore State** commands allow the state of the simulation to be saved at any time and then later restored, allowing you to rerun the simulation from a known point. The Save command causes the current time value, the value of all signals, and copies of all signal events occurring at the current time or later to be saved. The Restore command clears all pending events and replaces them with the ones on the save list, then resets the signal states and current time to the saved values.

Each saved event is associated with some signal in the circuit. If the circuit is modified after a Save State is done, some of the signals associated with these events may be destroyed or merged with other signals. Each time such a modification is made, the saved-event list is updated accordingly, but you should be aware that this may cause some events to be removed from the list.

An alternative method of replaying input stimulus is to use the Cut and Paste commands in the timing window. These operations associate events with signals by name and will therefore work between totally different circuits so long as the names match. For more information, see Chapter 8, Simulation.

Clear Timing

Selecting the **Clear Timing** command clears the timing window, removes all scheduled signal events, and recalculates output values for all circuit elements.

Clear Unknowns

Selecting the **Clear Unknowns** command clears all flip-flop, counter, and register primitives to the "0" state and attempts to remove all unknown signal values from the circuit. Note that certain circuit conditions may prevent signals from being placed in a known state:

■ Unconnected inputs that have not be set to a known level

■ Storage devices, such as RAMs that have an unknown stored value

■ Any simulation model that does not produce a known output when all inputs are known

Timing Display Options

Timing Display Resolution

The **Timing Options** command allows you to set the resolution of the timing display and select from a number of options for the positioning of "graticule" reference marks. The default resolution is 2 screen dots per time unit, but this can be adjusted over the range of 4 dots per time unit to 10 time units per dot. The reference marks may be disabled, placed at fixed time intervals, or placed at points where the currently selected signal rises or falls. These lines are intended to assist in comparing relative timing of signals on a timing diagram.

Timing Edge Reference Lines

The "Falling edge," "Rising edge of signal CLK," and "Both edges" selections will be enabled only if a named signal is currently selected. If one of the three edge options is already selected and you wish to change to a different signal, you must first select the "None" option, then OK, to cancel the current signal reference; then select the desired reference signal on the circuit diagram, select the Timing Options command again, and select the desired edge option.

Timing Data Retention

These options allow you to determine how much signal event data is retained in memory when a simulation is run.

Each time a signal-level change occurs, LogicWorks creates a record in memory containing a reference to the signal, time, new value, and source of the change. In a large simulation these records can consume enormous amounts of memory. This data can be retained for the following purposes:

- For use in refreshing the timing window should it become hidden and then be redisplayed

- For use in timing-window editing operations, such as taking the output from one circuit and using it as stimulus for another

Note that data can be retained only for signals displayed in the timing window. Signal event data for all other signals is discarded immediately after it is no longer required for simulation.

The option "Retain displayed range only" is the normal default and results in data being discarded immediately after the corresponding point on the timing display scrolls off the left-hand side. This results in minimal memory usage. The setting is equivalent to entering 0 in the "Retain for x time units" box.

The option "Retain for x time units" allows you to keep the signal event data for the specified amount of time after it scrolls off the left side of the screen. If this results in a memory shortage, the simulation will stop and a message will be displayed.

Creating and Editing PROMs and PLA Devices

The **New PROM or PLA** command allows you to define the internal logic for your own devices using either PROM (truth table) or PLA (product term) format. Because this is a major topic, it is covered in depth in Chapter 9, PROM and PLA Devices.

Creating RAM Devices

The **New RAM** command allows you to create fully simulated RAM devices in a variety of storage and control pin configurations. RAM devices are covered in Chapter 10, Primitive Devices.

Editing Devices

The **Edit Internals** command allows you to edit the internal logic of the selected PROM or PLA after it has been placed in the circuit. This command will also be available for devices containing editable PLAs, such as Programmable Logic Device macros.

Set Params

The **Set Params** command is a general method of setting parameters and options that are associated with the various types of objects in LogicWorks. If no objects are selected in the circuit, Set Params will be disabled. If more than one object is selected in the circuit, Set Params will display the following Parameters box:

```
┌─────────────────────────────────────────────────────┐
│  Change status of selected objects                   │
│  All objects:                                        │
│   Omit from report:        ○ Set  ○ Clear  ◉ No change│
│                                                      │
│  Signals only:                                       │
│   Display in timing diagram:  ○ Set  ○ Clear  ◉ No change│
│   Stuck value:                ○ Set  ○ Clear  ◉ No change│
│                              ( Cancel )  (( Change ))  │
└─────────────────────────────────────────────────────┘
```

Any of the four options in this box can be turned on (Set), turned off (Clear), or left in their current state (No change). The first two options apply to all devices and signals selected, the latter two apply only to signals.

Omit from Report

When this option is set, the selected objects will not appear in any netlists, component lists, or other output from the Report module. This can be used, for example, to effectively hide devices that are added to a schematic for simulation purposes only and would not form part of a finished product.

Display in Timing Diagram

This option allows you to add or remove the selected signals from the timing display.

NOTE: If the timing window is active, this is the only option available.

Stuck Value

If this option is turned on, all selected signals will be placed in the "stuck" state, that is, the signal values will not change as a result of device reevaluations on that net.

Single-Object Set Params

If a single object is selected, Set Params displays a box specific to the object type. Detailed information on the parameter entry requirements for each type is found in the following sections:

> Devices: Chapter 7, Devices
>
> Signals: Chapter 6, Signals
>
> Text: Chapter 5, Creating the Schematic

To leave the Set Params dialog box, click on the OK button or press ⏎Enter .

Show Circuit Info

This item displays circuit statistics such as number of devices, number of signals, number of from-to interconnects, and available memory. Selecting the **Show Circuit Info** command displays the following dialog box:

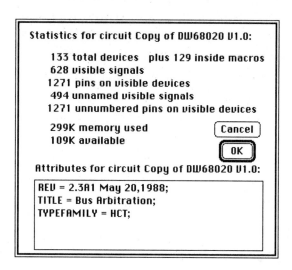

```
Statistics for circuit Copy of DW68020 U1.0:

    133 total deuices   plus 129 inside macros
    628 uisible signals
    1271 pins on uisible deuices
    494 unnamed uisible signals
    1271 unnumbered pins on uisible deuices

    299K memory used          [ Cancel ]
    109K auailable            [  OK  ]

Attributes for circuit Copy of DW68020 U1.0:

    REU = 2.3A1 May 20,1988;
    TITLE = Bus Arbitration;
    TYPEFAMILY = HCT;
```

The counts of "unnamed visible signals" and "unnumbered pins" are provided for cases where it is desired to produce a netlist from the circuit data. Any unnamed signal will be given a program-assigned name in the netlist, and any unnumbered pins will appear as "?".

The "memory used" figure roughly indicates the size of the circuit once it is saved to disk, but does not include dynamic information such as signal events. Note that "memory used" and "available" will not always add up to a constant total due to allocation and deallocation of internal program data.

The circuit Attributes box is a block of text data up to 32,000 characters long that is stored with the circuit file. It can be used for the following purposes:

- ▓ Storing random notations that you do not want to display on the diagram itself.

- ▓ Inserting global parameters in circuit reports (for SPICE netlist output, for example). See Chapter 13, Creating Text Reports, for more information on attribute formats.

Device Orientation

The **Device Orientation** command sets the orientation (up, down, left, right, mirrored) that will be used next time a device is created or a circuit scrap is pasted. Each time this command is selected, the current setting is rotated 90° counterclockwise. The current setting is indicated by the small device symbol in the lower-left corner of the window. The orientation can also be changed by clicking directly on the Orientation icon or using the arrow keys on the keyboard. See Chapter 5, Creating the Schematic, for more information about orientation.

12

The Device Editor

Introduction

The Device Editor is a module used to create device symbols or general graphics (title blocks or mechanical drawings, for example) for use on LogicWorks schematics. It provides a complete, object-oriented drawing environment with standard drawing tools, as well as specific functions tailored for symbol creation.

Entering the Device Editor

To invoke the Device Editor, select DevEditor from the Module menu. This will open an empty graphics window, allowing you to create a new device type from scratch.

Creating a New Device Type

Selecting DevEditor from the Module menu opens an empty drawing window with a default name and an empty pin list, as shown below. You can then create the symbol using the drawing tools provided and add pins using the pin tools in the tool palette.

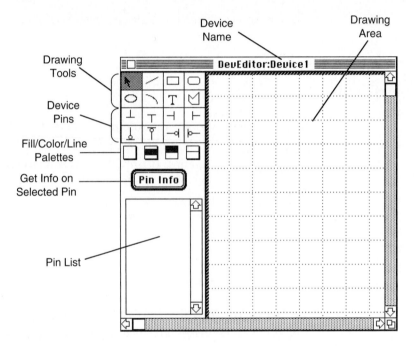

Drawing Tools

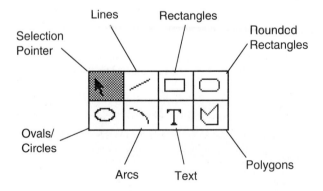

If you plan to associate an internal circuit with the symbol for simulation or hierarchical netlisting purposes, you should select the internal circuit before adding any pins to the symbol.

Note that each time you place a pin, a new default name is added to the pin list. This name can be changed using the Pin Info button. Sequences of names (such as D0, D1, and D2) can be added using the Add Pins command from the DevEditor menu (discussed later in this chapter).

The newly created device type is written to a library using the Save Type To command from the File menu.

Editing an Existing Type

To edit an existing device type in a library, open the Device Editor by selecting DevEditor from the Module menu, then use the Open Type command from the File menu.

Selecting an Internal Circuit

In order to associate an internal circuit with a symbol, the circuit must first be open in a LogicWorks circuit window. Once the circuit is open, select the Internal Circuit command from the DevEditor menu, or select the Set Primitive Type command and double-click on the Macro item in the type list. This will display a list of the open circuits, allowing you to choose the desired one. It is best to do this before the symbol is drawn so that the list of pin signals in the internal circuit is handy in the pin list.

Once an internal circuit is selected, the circuit is scanned for named signals that will act as pin connections on the new symbol. The pin list will then display all signals in the internal circuit that are available to be used as external pins. You can then use the AutoSym command to generate a symbol based on the given names, or you can select these names one at a time and place a corresponding pin object in the drawing window. It is not necessary to assign all internal signals to pins.

IMPORTANT: Note that the following types of internal signals *cannot* be used as pin connections and will not show in the pin list:

- Signals named "0" or "1"
- Any signal connected to another by name

Device Pins

The top row of device pin tools is used to create device pins on the symbol in any of four orientations. If the name of an unplaced pin is selected in the pin list, the next pin placed with one of these tools will be that item. If no pin name is selected, or if the selected item has already been placed, adding one of these pins will create a new entry in the pin list with the name "PINxx" where xx is a sequential number. This name can be changed using the Pin Info button.

The second row of pins is provided as a way to create pins with an inversion bubble. Using one of these actually places two separate objects: the pin and the circle. Once placed, these will remain associated during this editing session, so they are moved and deleted together. Once the type has been saved in a library, they become independent entities and can be moved and manipulated separately. A pin created with the inverted pin tools has no special characteristics; these are provided only as a graphical convenience.

Pin Info Button

The Pin Info button allows you to view and set information about a pin. Clicking on it brings up the following dialog box:

Pin Name

The Pin Name box allows you to edit the name of the pin. Pin names can be up to 15 characters and have the following functions in LogicWorks:

■ The pin name is used to match the pin with an associated signal in an internal circuit. If this pin is associated with an internal signal, changing the name here will remove that connection. This pin will then be floating unless the name change causes it to become attached to another internal signal.

■ Pin names are used in some types of reports to provide a symbolic reference to a pin.

Pin Number

The Pin Number value is a string of up to four characters that appears adjacent to the pin when the device is used in a LogicWorks circuit. The string entered here is only a default value; the number can be edited in the circuit diagram.

Placed

The Placed item will have a check mark next to it if the pin in question has been placed on the symbol. Information about any pins that have not been placed is lost when the type is closed.

Signal

The Signal item will have a check mark next to it if this pin is associated with a signal in an internal circuit.

Pin Type

The Pin Type buttons allow you to set the type ("Input", "Output", and so on) of a pin on a primitive (non-macro) device. If the primitive type has not been set, the device is assumed to be a macro type and these items will be disabled. Pin types for macros are determined by the logic of the internal circuit (if any) or are set to "Input" if none. (See the "Set Primitive Type" section later in this chapter.)

If the pin type on a primitive device is set incorrectly, the simulator will generate incorrect results and may produce error messages when signal-level changes are assigned by the model code.

Pin List

The Pin List box contains a scrollable list of the pin names associated with this device type. This list is derived from the following sources:

- If the symbol was opened from an existing entry in a library, the initial list will be the pins on the existing type.

- If a pin tool is clicked in the symbol-drawing area while no pin name is selected in the list, a new item is added with the name "PINxx" where xx is a sequential number.

- If an open LogicWorks circuit is selected as a macro internal circuit, the name of any signal meeting the requirements for a pin connection will be added to the list (in other words, no "0" or "1" and no connection by name).

- The Add Pins commands can be used to add sequential lists of numbered pins to the list.

- The AutoSym command can be used to specify all the pins and pin numbering for a device symbol.

Any pin that has been placed so that a corresponding graphical pin object appears on the symbol will have a "•" mark beside it. Information about any unplaced pins is lost when the device type is closed.

Shift Key Usage

The ⇧Shift key serves two purposes in the Device Editor:

- Holding down ⇧Shift while clicking on an object adds to the current selection (in other words, selects the object without deselecting the other selected objects).

- Holding down ⇧Shift while drawing a line constrains the line to multiples of 45°.

The DevEditor Menu

The **DevEditor menu** is available when the module is active, and includes the following options:

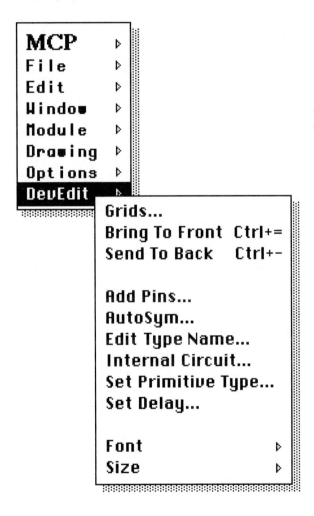

Grids

This command allows you to specify the visible and snap-to grids for objects drawn using the drawing tools.

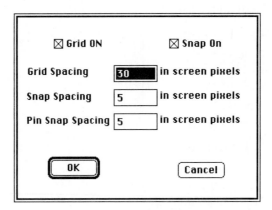

Grid On

This checkbox determines whether visible grid lines are shown in the drawing window. The spacing between these grid lines is determined by the Grid Spacing box below.

Snap On

This checkbox determines whether the corners of drawn objects are snapped to the nearest grid point.

Grid Spacing

This number determines the spacing between the visible grid lines, given in screen dots.

Snap Spacing

This number determines the spacing between snap-to points for general drawing tools (not including pins). This does not affect objects that have already been placed.

Pin Snap Spacing

This number determines the snap-to grid for device pins. This must be a multiple of 5 to meet the LogicWorks pin grid requirements.

Bring To Front and Send To Back

These commands are used to set the front-to-back ordering of the selected objects relative to the other graphics objects. This will only affect the appearance of objects with fill patterns.

Add Pins

This command is an alternative method of adding numbered sequences of pins to the pin list.

NOTE: It is not necessary to use this command for single pins, since they are added to the list automatically when a pin is placed in the drawing area.

```
┌──────────────────────────────────────────┐
│                                          │
│           Create Device Pins             │
│                                          │
│  Pin names to start from:  ┌──────────┐  │
│                            │ D0       │  │
│  Number of pins to create: ┌──────────┐  │
│                            │ 16       │  │
│                                          │
│    ┌─────────┐          ┌─────────┐      │
│    │  Add    │          │ Cancel  │      │
│    └─────────┘          └─────────┘      │
│                                          │
└──────────────────────────────────────────┘
```

In the "Pin names to start from" box, enter the name of the first pin desired. This will normally have a numeric part, such as "D0", "FC8", or the like. In the "Number of pins to create" box, enter the number of pins desired in the sequence.

When you click on the Add button, the list of pin names specified will be added to the pin list in the main drawing window. These items can then be selected and placed manually.

AutoSym

This command invokes the automatic symbol generator, which is described in detail later in this chapter.

Edit Type Name

This command allows you to change the type name, that is, the name under which the type will be saved in a library.

Internal Circuit

This command allows you to select one of the currently open LogicWorks circuits to become the internal circuit for this macro. If the desired internal circuit is not open, it must be opened first (by selecting Drawing from the Module menu, then using the Open Circuit command) before it can be attached to the symbol.

Set Primitive Type

This command allows you to specify that the new device type should take on the characteristics of one of the LogicWorks simulation primitives.

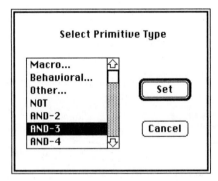

Set Delay

This command allows you the set the default delay for this device type. This delay value can always be overridden in each individual instance of the device in a LogicWorks circuit.

Font and Size

These items set the text characteristics for the selected text objects and all text objects created thereafter.

The File Menu

New Type

The New Type command opens up a new, empty DevEditor window.

Open Type

The Open Type command allows you to select any device from an open library for editing.

Close Type

The Close Type command closes the current DevEditor window. If any changes have been made to the open device type, you will be prompted to save or discard the changes.

Save Type

The Save Type command saves the contents of the current DevEditor window back to the library it was read from. If the open type was not read from a library—that is, it was newly created—this item will be disabled.

Save Type To

The Save Type To command will bring up the following dialog box, allowing you to select the library to save the current device type to or to create a new library.

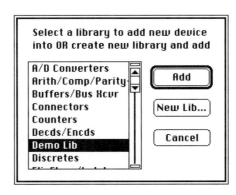

Edit Menu

The standard Edit menu commands Cut, Copy, and Paste can be used to move objects between DevEditor windows, and to and from LogicWorks circuit windows.

Automatic Symbol Generator

The AutoSym menu item invokes the Automatic Symbol Generator, which will create standard rectangular symbols given a list of the desired input and output pins. For maximum flexibility, the symbol generated using AutoSym consists of separate graphics objects and is completely editable after it is generated.

The current settings for text font and size are used in generating the symbol. The only exception to this is the type name text placed in the center of the symbol, which is written 3 points larger than the current setting and in bold.

Selecting the AutoSym command displays the following dialog box:

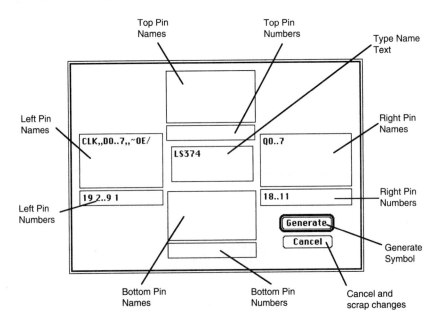

The pin name and number boxes will contain information derived from the existing pin list, if any. These can be modified as desired and the new settings will completely replace any old names or numbers when the Generate button is pressed.

Specifying Pin Names

The four pin name boxes allow you to specify the names of pins to appear on the left, right, top, and bottom of the device symbol. The following options are available to assist in specifying pin names and appearance:

- Sequences of names with a numeric part can be specified with the ".." (two periods) notation shown above, so that:

  D0..7   means   D0 D1 D2 D3 D4 D5 D6 D7

  IPL0/..2 means   IPL0/ IPL1/ IPL2/

  A15..0   means   A15 A14 A13 ...

Note that the numeric part does not have to be at the end of the name string.

- Inverted pins can be specified using the "~" character in front of the name, as shown in the "OE/" name in the AutoSym dialog box on the facing page. The "~" will not appear in the symbol.

- Items in a list can be separated by blanks or commas. Placing an extra comma between two items adds spacing between the pins on the symbol. This is illustrated in the input pins in the example.

Pin names can be up to 16 characters long.

Specifying Pin Numbers

The four pin-number boxes allow you to specify pin numbers corresponding to the pin name sequences. The pin numbers must be matched one-for-one with the pin names in the name sequence. The only special convention for pin numbering is the ".." sequence notation exactly as described for pin names above. Pin numbers can be up to four characters long and can contain any printable characters.

Type Name Text

The Type Name text box allows you to specify the text that will appear centered at the top of the symbol.

Generate

The Generate button causes the current contents of the active drawing window and pin list to be erased and replaced by the generated symbol. This symbol consists of standard graphic objects, so it can be edited using any of the drawing tools provided.

The entries shown in the AutoSym dialog box above produce the following symbol in the drawing window:

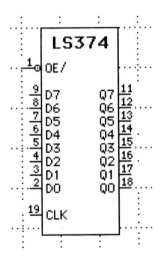

13

Creating
Text Reports

The **Report** command from the Module menu allows you to generate a text file containing information about the current circuit. When this command is selected, the following dialog box is displayed:

Report Type	⦿ Signals ◯ Devices ◯ Types ◯ SPICE
Combine pins on same device	◯ On ⦿ Off
Item separator	⦿ Blank ◯ Tab
Column formatting	◯ On ⦿ Off
Include null signals	◯ On ⦿ Off
Max. line width	255
Max. lines/page	50

OK   Cancel

◯ Commercial SPICE   ◯ Berkeley SPICE

Report Format Options

Report Type

The Signals report type produces a netlist file containing a list of the signals in the circuit. Each entry gives the name of the signal followed by the device pin connections made by that signal. Unnamed signals will have a default name assigned in the form "S00001", "S00002", and so on. Unnumbered pins will show in the list as "?". Entries are sorted in order by signal name. The Set Params command "Omit from report" option allows you to selectively omit items from the report.

The Devices report type produces a file containing a list of the devices in the circuit, sorted by name. Each line in the file consists of the device name followed by its type (the type name as it appears in the Libraries menu). Unnamed devices will have a default name assigned in the form "D00001", "D00002", and so on.

The Types report type produces a list in which each line represents one device type used in the circuit, giving the type name, the number used, and the names of all devices of that type.

The SPICE report type produces a netlist file suitable for any analog simulator based on SPICE. When this type is selected, the two option buttons at the bottom of the box will be enabled. These options are explained in the next section.

Combine Pins on Same Device

This option, when on, tells the Report Generator to combine all pins for a single device attached to one signal into a single entry. For example, instead of:

```
IC1-1 IC1-33 IC1-34
```

the combined entry would appear as:

```
IC1-1,33,34
```

This produces a more user-readable report for layout or wiring purposes.

Item Separator

This option allows you to select either a tab or blank to space the items on a line. The tab separator can be used to produce a format that can be read by a spreadsheet or file management program.

Column Formatting

When enabled, this option inserts extra spaces between items to create a neatly formatted list when printed with a fixed-space font.

Include Null Signals

This option applies to the Signals type only. When "on" is selected, all signals will be included in the report, even if they have less than two pin connections.

Max. Line Width

This setting determines the maximum number of characters that will be written on a line before inserting a return in the file. It must be in the range 1 to 32,767. Set it to a large number (such as 30,000) to allow any number of entries on a line without returns.

Max. Lines/Page

This setting determines the maximum number of lines that will be written into a file before a form feed character is inserted. This character is interpreted by most word processing programs as "new page." To get continuous output without form feeds, set this to a large number (such as 30,000).

Creating Netlists for SPICE

When the SPICE report type is selected, LogicWorks will generate a netlist suitable as input for any simulator based on the SPICE package from the University of California at Berkeley. The discussion of format options below assumes that you have at least a basic knowledge of the SPICE netlist format.

SPICE Format Options

Because there are some variations in the SPICE format, LogicWorks allows you to select one of two styles:

Commercial SPICE

Clicking on this option button causes the Report module to generate a SPICE netlist that uses the signal names assigned on the schematic for node names. Most commercial SPICE packages, such as PSPICE™ from MicroSim, will accept arbitrary alphanumeric names for nodes. The only exception is the ground node, which must be called "0" (zero). It is the user's responsibility to use the SPICE Ground device to mark the common node or to name it "0" using the normal naming methods.

Berkeley SPICE

This option causes LogicWorks to generate a SPICE file that uses numbers arbitrarily assigned to all nodes. The original Berkeley version of SPICE and some commercial SPICEs, such as IntuSoft SPICE, require this format. The disadvantage of this format is that it is much more difficult to edit the netlist file directly, because the signal names have been removed.

Certain naming conventions must be followed in creating circuits for use with SPICE, and variations may exist depending on which version of SPICE you are using.

Device Libraries for SPICE

Any symbols can be used to create SPICE netlists so long as the correct pin order is observed. If you wish to create your own symbols for use with

SPICE, see the section below on pin order considerations. In the standard Discretes library supplied with LogicWorks, the pin order has been set up to match SPICE usage. Several devices appear in the Discretes library that are specifically designed for SPICE:

SPICE Ground

This is a standard ground symbol except that the pin name has been changed so that the attached signal is automatically named "0", the standard name for the SPICE common node.

SPICE Resistor and SPICE Coil

These devices are standard resistor and inductor symbols except that a mark has been added, denoting the positive end for current flow measurements. If the standard resistor symbol is used, it is difficult to be sure that it is placed in the correct orientation on the schematic so that the pins appear in the correct order in the netlist.

Device and Signal (Node) Naming for SPICE

Device Naming

In SPICE, the first letter of the device name determines its type, as in "R1" for a resistor or "VIN" for a voltage source. This name can be applied to the device on the diagram using the usual LogicWorks naming method, as follows:

- Select the pencil cursor from the tool palette.

- Press and hold the mouse button on the device in question.

- Drag to where you want the name to appear and release the mouse button.

- Type the desired name and press ⏎Enter.

This name will appear first on each device line in the netlist file.

Signal (Node) Naming

SPICE uses the special node name "0" (the integer zero) to denote the ground or common point in the circuit. This name must be explicitly applied to the diagram using the Name command in order to appear correctly in the netlist. Most current commercial versions of SPICE allow arbitrary alphanumeric names for all except the ground node. This means you can allow LogicWorks to assign default names to unnamed nodes using its standard "S00001" format. Nodes that are important measuring points for your simulation should be explicitly named in a more meaningful way, such as "VIN" or "VOUT".

In older versions of SPICE, node names were restricted to decimal integers, with the name "0" being used for the ground or common node. If your version requires strictly numeric names, you can either name all nodes on the diagram yourself or allow it to assign arbitrary numeric names in the netlist.

Note that node and device names are completely distinct and unrelated in LogicWorks. For example, if you place a voltage source device on the diagram and label it "VIN", its output node will not automatically inherit the name. If you wish to call the corresponding output node "VIN", it must be explicitly named using the Name command.

Associating SPICE Parameters with Devices

LogicWorks allows any arbitrary text data to be associated with any device or net using the "attribute" mechanism. This can be used to store and display SPICE parameters which are passed to the netlist, as follows:

- Select the device by clicking on it with the arrow cursor.

- Select the Set Params ([Ctrl]-i) command from the Options menu. A Parameters dialog box appears.

- Click in the Attributes text box.

- Type your parameters in the form "SPICE=*params*;". If you want the "*params*" text to be displayed on the diagram, add a "¦" character at the end of the entry, as in "SPICE=*params*;¦" (see the example on the opposite page).

- Click on the OK button.

This text is now associated with the device and will be stored with the circuit file. It can be edited at any time by repeating the Set Params command. If you included the "¦" marker, the text between the "=" and the ";" will appear under the device name on the diagram.

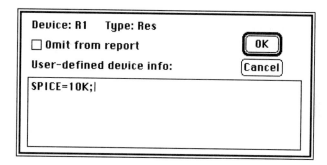

It is also frequently desirable to store parameters that are global to the whole circuit and not associated with any particular device. These can be used to store simulation parameters and SPICE control information with the circuit file. This can be done using the circuit attribute block, accessed by using the Show Circuit Info command in LogicWorks, as in the following example:

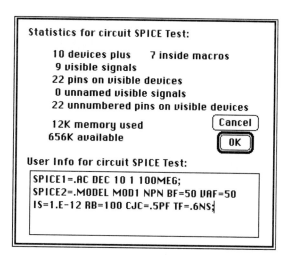

In the standard SPICE report format supplied with LogicWorks, any lines contained in the field "SPICE1" will be inserted before the device list, and lines in "SPICE2" will be inserted after the device list.

Creating Device Symbols for Use with SPICE

LogicWorks is shipped with a set of libraries of the common discrete components which can be used for creating SPICE schematics. This section describes the procedure for creating new symbols and adding them to the existing libraries. This is easily done using the methods described in the Device Librarian manual. The only special consideration for SPICE concerns the order in which the pins are defined.

When a SPICE-format netlist is produced, each line consists of a device name, followed by a list of the nodes associated with the device. LogicWorks places the node names in the order that the pins appear in the pin list when the device is opened with the Device Librarian. The order of this node list must match the order assumed by SPICE for the given device type.

For example, to create a transistor symbol for use with SPICE, it is necessary to determine the node order expected. This information is given in the SPICE manual as Collector, Base, Emitter. The procedure for creating the library entry is as follows (see Chapter 12, The Device Editor, for more details):

- ▦ Select DevEditor from the Module menu.

- ▦ Draw the desired symbol graphics or use the Paste command to place graphics created elsewhere. The window should now appear as follows:

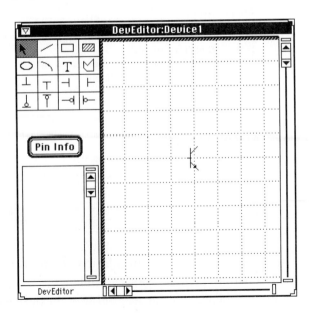

■ You now have to place the Collector pin on the symbol. Click on the up-facing pin in the tool palette (or whichever pin direction is appropriate for the collector in your symbol):

■ Place the pin at the collector position on the symbol:

■ Select the appropriate pin tool and place the Base pin.

■ Select the appropriate pin tool and place the Emitter pin.

NOTE: The order of placement is important!

■ Click on the name PIN1 in the pin list and then click the Pin Info button. Change the name of PIN1 to C (for Collector).

■ Similarly, change PIN2 to B and PIN3 to E. The window should now look as follows:

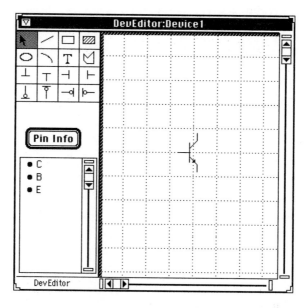

■ Save the device in the usual way using the Save Type To command.

SPICE Netlist Example

The following circuit illustrates the naming and attribute conventions described above. This circuit is supplied on the LogicWorks disk under the name "SPICE". Use the Show Circuit Info command to observe the entry of SPICE parameters for the circuit, and the Set Params command for device parameters.

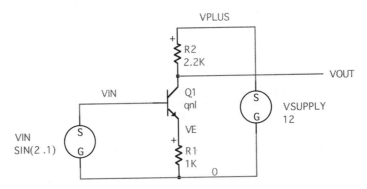

All the devices used in this example are found in the Discretes library:

Symbol	Library Part Name
Resistor	SPICE Resistor
Transistor	NPN
Source	Ind. Volt. Source

The following entries were made in the circuit attributes block using the Show Circuit Info command:

```
SPICE1=.tran lus lms;
SPICE2=.model qnl npn(bf=80 rb=100
ccs=2pf tf=0.3ns
+ tr=6ns cje=3pf cjc=2pf va=50);
```

These items can be typed directly in the box or pasted using Ctrl-V. Note that returns can be typed in an attribute field.

SPICE Fomat Notes

- ■ The "+" symbol is the SPICE continuation mark.

- ■ Each attribute field can contain any number of lines separated by returns.

- ■ Everything between the "=" after the field name and the following ";" will appear verbatim in the output file. A field *can* contain "=" but *cannot* contain ";" because this is the terminator.

Each device has had SPICE parameters entered using the Set Params box, as in the following example of the VIN device:

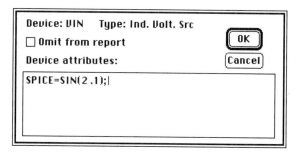

This circuit produces the following SPICE netlist file using the Commercial SPICE option:

```
SPICE Monday October 21, 1991 5:48 PM Commercial SPICE
.PROBE
.tran lus lms
Q1 VOUT VIN VE qnl
R1 VE 0 1K
R2 VPLUS VOUT 2.2K
VIN VIN 0 SIN(2 .1)
VSUPPLY VPLUS 0 12
.model qnl npn(bf=80 rb=100 ccs=2pf tf=0.3ns
+ tr=6ns cje=3pf cjc=2pf va=50)
.end
```

14

The Parts Window

The **parts window** allows access to the device libraries used with LogicWorks. Devices can be taken from the parts window and placed on the circuit page. The parts window also allows access to maintenance routines.

Parts Menu

The parts window has its own menu. This menu can be accessed in two ways. The first is through the Libraries item from the File menu. The second is by holding down [Ctrl] while pressing the mouse button (not the menu button) over the parts window. This will bring up a pop-up menu over the parts window.

There are four items in the Parts/Libraries menu:

New Lib

New Lib displays a dialog box with a default name and directory list. Change the name and directory as appropriate for your new library. Click on the Save button when you have set the correct name and directory. The new library will be saved to disk and will become the currently open library, as displayed in the parts window. The library will be empty to begin with.

Open Lib

Open Lib will display a dialog box showing the names of library files in the current directory. Change to the directory containing the library file you wish to open, select the name, and click on the Open button or double-click on the name. This will become the currently open library and will be displayed in the parts window.

Close Lib

Close Lib displays a dialog box with all the names of the libraries currently open in LogicWorks. Select one by clicking on the name and clicking the Close button. You can also select a group of names by clicking on the first name, then holding down ⇧Shift and clicking on the last name in the group. You can also select or deselect names by holding down Ctrl and clicking on the name.

Lib Maint

Lib Maint allows you to manipulate libraries once they are made. The libraries to be manipulated must be open.

The Library Maintenance Dialog Box

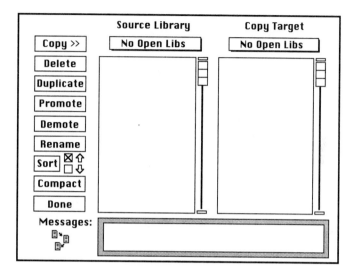

The Library Maintenance dialog box can work with one or two libraries at a time. The first library is the "source." The second is the "target," used only for copying from the source. To work on a specific source library, click on the title block (initially showing "No Open Libs") and select the source library. If you are going to copy devices into a target library, do the same for the target's title block. With the source library (and possibly a target library) open, the device parts can be manipulated as follows:

Copy

Select the devices to be copied from the source library. Click on the Copy >> button. The selected devices will be copied to the target library.

Delete

Select the devices to be deleted and click on the Delete button. These devices will be removed from the source or target library.

Duplicate

Select the devices to be duplicated within the source library. Click on the Duplicate button. A dialog box will now be displayed so that you can rename the duplicates or skip the device. You must change the duplicate's name so that it is unique in the library. The duplicate part will be added to the end of the library list.

Promote and Demote

Select the devices you wish to move to a different position in the library list. Click on the Promote button to move the devices up one position. Click on the Demote button to move the devices down one position.

Rename

Select the devices to be renamed. Click on the Rename button. A dialog box will now be displayed so that you can rename each selected device or skip past it. The device names must be unique in the library.

Sort

The Sort button will sort the entire library, not just the selected devices. Click in the box beside the arrow pointing up to sort in ascending order. Click in the box beside the arrow pointing down to sort in descending order.

Compact

When libraries are manipulated, devices are never actually moved to or removed from the library; information specifying these operations is merely added to the library file. For this reason, it is possible to remove numerous parts from the library yet gain no file size advantage, because the devices were never actually removed from the file. The Compact command will solve this problem by copying only valid devices from the source library into the target library. The target must be opened before compaction.

Done

When all operations are completed, click on the Done button.

Appendix

Setup File Format

The first word of each statement is a keyword that specifies a setup option. Statements are terminated by a semicolon and can contain embedded comments in braces, as in { Comment }. LogicWorks recognizes the following keywords:

Library and Circuit Folder

```
FOLDER folderName;
```

This specifies the directory/folder that will contain the libraries to be specified in following LIBRARY statements, or circuit files for the following CIRCUIT statements. This statement can be omitted if the files are in the same directory as LogicWorks, or if you prefer to specify a complete file pathname in each library statement. The FOLDER option does not actually change what the system thinks is the current directory; it just specifies a prefix to be added to subsequent library names. You can therefore specify multiple FOLDER statements, as in the example later in this section. Each one is valid until the next FOLDER statement. The following are valid statements:

```
FOLDER LIBS;
```

specifies a directory called Libs contained in the same directory that contains LogicWorks.

```
FOLDER \LWRKS\LIBS;
```

specifies a directory called LIBS in the LWRKS directory in the root directory.

```
FOLDER LIBS\7400Cnts:;
```

specifies a directory called 7400 Counters which is contained inside a directory called LIBS which is in the same directory as LogicWorks.

Default Libraries

```
LIBRARY libName;
```

This specifies the name of a library to open. The library will be opened each time LogicWorks is started up and its name will appear in the parts window. As discussed above, libName can be a simple filename or a complete pathname specifying the disk and directories containing the library. Note that the name specified in the last FOLDER statement is always attached to the front of the name specified in the LIBRARY statement, even if a complete pathname is given. Following are examples of acceptable LIBRARY statements (these all assume no FOLDER statement has been used):

```
LIBRARY LIBS\Counters;
```

specifies a library called Counters in the LIBS directory.

```
LIBRARY Discrete;
```

specifies a library called Discrete in the directory LogicWorks is in (or in the directory specified by the last FOLDER statement).

Default Circuit

```
CIRCUIT circuitName;
```

This statement allows you to specify a circuit file to open when the program starts. This can be used to open a file that is being repeatedly edited or to open a default template file with a standard title block or border. Also, you can specify a circuit file to open on the command line when you first run LogicWorks.

Timing Window Settings

Trace Width

FATTRACES;

The FATTRACES option doubles the "pen width" used to draw traces in the timing diagram.

Trace Fill

SOLIDTRACES;

This keyword causes the fill patterns for High Impedance, Don't Know, and Conflict states to be set to solid.

Simulation Disable Options

Macro Internal Circuits

NOSIMLOAD;

The NOSIMLOAD keyword is used to disable the loading of simulation information when devices are read from libraries. This will result in dramatic reductions in file size when LogicWorks is to be used only for schematic entry and the simulation function is not required.

WARNING: Once a schematic is created with this option, it will be completely devoid of simulation information. Removing this keyword from the Setup file *will not* make the circuit file simulatable. The only way to restore the simulation data is to delete all the device symbols and reread them from the libraries. (A device reload capability will be incorporated in future versions of LogicWorks.)

The NOSIMLOAD option affects devices only as they are read from a library. It has *no* effect on:

■ An existing file containing simulation models

■ Clipboard operations on devices in a circuit already containing simulation models

■ Primitive devices, because their simulation models are hard-coded in the program

Hide Timing Window

```
NOSIMDISPLAY;
```

The NOSIMDISPLAY keyword is used to set the default simulation status when a new circuit is created. This option has no permanent effect on the file or the circuit data. When the NOSIMDISPLAY keyword appears in the Setup file, a circuit created using the New command will occupy the entire screen, the timing window will be hidden, and the simulation status will be set to Pause. The timing window can be redisplayed using the Window menu, and the simulation status can be set using the normal menu or tool palette commands.

Internal Error Checking

```
NOERRORCHECK;
```

This option disables the internal error checking described later in the Appendix. This should only be done in consultation with our Technical Support department, because it will prevent warnings from being issued for internal or unusual system errors. In many cases, these errors can be easily recovered if corrected immediately but may cause data corruption if left undetected.

File-Naming Conventions

LogicWorks uses two file-naming conventions: All circuit files will have a .CCT extension; all libraries will have a .CLF extension. If a file is named with the wrong extension, it will not be found by the Open dialog box. As a rule, LogicWorks will always force the issue, but if you change the name outside of LogicWorks, the file will not be found the next time LogicWorks is run.

LogicWorks uses other extensions for reports, but these are never read back in to LogicWorks and so can be changed as desired.

Inside LogicWorks

LogicWorks performs a discrete simulation of the signal changes in a logic circuit, meaning that signal levels and time change only in steps, rather than continuously. The program does not attempt to analyze your circuit, but simply tracks signal-level changes through the devices. Thus, circuits with feedback loops or other delay-dependent features should be simulated correctly so long as they don't rely on particular analog characteristics of devices.

The simulation is "event driven," an event being a change in the level of a signal. Each time an event occurs, a list is made of all the devices whose inputs are affected by that event. Any other events occurring at the same time are similarly evaluated, and affected devices added to the list. A type-specific routine is then called for each device on the change list in order to determine what output changes are going to occur. These changes are added to the event list, their time of occurrence depending upon the device delay. No computation is performed for times when no event occurs, so device delay settings and clock values have no effect on how fast the simulation is performed.

LogicWorks performs strictly a digital simulation. It does not take into account factors such as fan-out (the number of inputs connected to a given output), line length (capacitance), or asymmetrical output drive, except inasmuch as these affect delay time.

Time Values

Time values are stored internally using 32-bit integers, but integer overflow is avoided by detecting when time is approaching a maximum value and then resetting all time values relative to zero. It is convenient to think of the time values as being in nanoseconds, but the interpretation is left to the user.

For any primitive device with a delay characteristic, the delay value can be set to any integer between 0 and 32,767. The zero value is a special case, and should only be used with an understanding of how the simulation is performed, as described above. In particular, note that on a given pass through the simulation routine all the events on the list that occur at the current time are scanned, then the new outputs for all affected devices are calculated. If any of these devices has a zero delay setting, this will result in more changes being placed on the event list at the current time. All these changes emerging from zero-delay devices will not be evaluated, however, until the next pass through the simulator. This is done to allow for user interaction with the simulation.

If a zero-delay feedback loop exists in a circuit, the signal changes will be simulated, and any probes on the diagram will be updated at each pass through the simulator. The events at the head of the list, however, will always have the same time value associated with them, and the simulated time will never advance. This means that the updating of the timing window stops until some delay is inserted in the loop. Note also that the Pause control will appear not to work, since it does not actually disable the simulator but only prevents it from advancing to events at a time later than the current one.

Macro Devices

When a macro device is selected from a library, the device symbol and internal circuit are read into memory and retained with the circuit, even if the library is subsequently closed. Each time an incarnation of that device is created, the internal circuitry is duplicated, but not displayed. Macro device information is also stored with the circuit when it is saved to disk, so the library does not need to be accessible when the circuit is read in. Macros can be nested within other macros, but since all the internals are duplicated for each device, this can lead to a massive proliferation of devices and signals, with resultant demands on memory and slowing of the simulation. Thus, it is preferable to use primitives and PLAs/PROMs wherever possible to implement macro device simulations.

Memory Usage

When a circuit is opened or created by LogicWorks, the circuit data is retained completely in the memory of your machine. Since the total memory available is fixed (until you buy your next memory expansion!), this places some limits on circuit size. Some particular operations in LogicWorks tend to consume large amounts of space, so it is possible to make better use of available memory by being aware of these memory-intensive operations.

Due to the complex internal memory structures used in the program, it is not really possible to determine exactly how many bytes will be used by this or that operation. We therefore offer the following general notes on memory usage:

Simulation

Each time a signal changes state, an event record is created in memory. If the signal is not being displayed in the timing diagram, this record is deallocated after the signal change has occurred. If the signal is being displayed, the record is retained in memory until that change has scrolled off the left-hand side of the timing diagram. As a result, the memory used by event records will increase when the number of displayed signals is increased or the resolution of the timing display is decreased. In a complex circuit with a lot of signal changes and a long time interval displayed in the timing diagram, it is quite possible to have 100K or more allocated to event records.

Macro Devices

As mentioned above, each time a macro device is used in a circuit, all the internal circuitry is replicated. For this reason, it is worth some care to ensure that the macro circuit is as compact as possible. Here are some guidelines:

- Use PLAs or PROMs where possible to implement internal circuitry; one of these devices doesn't take up much more memory than a gate but can replace many other devices.

- Avoid nesting macros within macros, because all the information for each internal device must be stored in the circuit.

- Use a minimal number of line segments when creating signal lines. Even though they are not duplicated every time, they are carried as overhead within the device definition.

Memory Fragmentation

Each time an object is created, edited, or deleted in LogicWorks, memory is allocated and deallocated as required. After a large number of operations have been performed, this can result in memory "fragmentation," that is, a large number of small free areas in memory. Even when a circuit is closed, the memory it occupied might not become available in a single block, because it may be using memory scattered in among other circuits and internally-used blocks. Thus, it is quite possible to save and close a file, then attempt to reopen the same file and receive the message "Insufficient memory" because there is no single block large enough to contain the circuit. In this case, it is necessary to quit the program and restart it to reinitialize the memory system.

Internal Error Detection

LogicWorks makes use of a number of complex internal data structures in order to maintain an up-to-date image of your circuit at all times. To assist in detecting problems due to hardware failures, program errors, or operating system errors, a code module has been added that checks these structures for consistency. This is done in the background while the program is idling and should normally be invisible to the user.

Should a problem be detected, a warning box similar to the following will be displayed:

 We have bad news. An internal data inconsistency has been detected. If you save your file immediately under a different name, without making any further changes you may be able to recover the data currently in memory.

Please note the values below, the action you were just performing and any other information you feel might be relevant and call us at the number given in the About box.

State: 2001 Address: 00000000

Sorry!

The "State" value is a code that specifies the type of problem detected, and the "Address" value is the memory address of the object that was in error. It is beyond the scope of this manual to discuss the meaning of all possible error codes and an estimate of their severity. In general, a State < 100 indicates a structural problem that is likely to cause a serious program malfunction if you proceed with editing. The warning box will appear only once if this type of error is detected, even if other errors occur later. The error-detection mechanism is reset when all circuit files are closed. States > 100 indicate unexpected situations detected in connection with some specific function and may or may not be serious. If the error disappears after a later check (due to an offending object being deleted, for example), you will be notified. This may occur if you delete the corrupted part of the circuit or if some other internal check succeeds in correcting the problem.

If you see this box in the course of normal program operation, save your circuit file immediately *under a different name* (so as not to wipe out your last good backup). Quitting the program and rereading the saved file may result in the problem being corrected due to the checking done in the I/O process. If you can isolate the problem to one specific object, try deleting that object and then recreating it. In any case, please contact our Technical Support department and provide as much information as you can about the situation that created the problem. We will help you in any way we can to recover any lost data.

Error checking can be disabled using the NOERRORCHECK Setup file option, described earlier in the Appendix. This should not be used under normal circumstances.

Keyboard Shortcuts

The Control Key

Following are the Ctrl key equivalents for various menu commands:

Ctrl -A	Select All		Ctrl -S	Save
Ctrl -B	Save As		Ctrl -T	Clear Timing
Ctrl -C	Copy		Ctrl -U	Clear Unknowns
Ctrl -D	Duplicate		Ctrl -V	Paste
Ctrl -E	Step		Ctrl -W	Walk
Ctrl -G	Go To Selection		Ctrl -X	Cut
Ctrl -H	Zap		Ctrl -Z	Undo
Ctrl -I	Set Params		Ctrl -[	Reduce
Ctrl -J	Device Orientation		Ctrl -]	Expand
Ctrl -K	Set Display Area		Ctrl -=	Normal Size
Ctrl -N	Name		Ctrl -/	Reduce to Fit
Ctrl -O	Open		Ctrl -;	Save State
Ctrl -Q	Quit		Ctrl -'	Restore State
Ctrl -R	Run		Ctrl -,	Edit Internals

Following are other uses of Ctrl :

■ In most scrolling file lists in dialog boxes (for example, the Close Lib command), Ctrl can be used to select multiple, nonconsecutive items.

■ When held down while drawing a signal line, Ctrl causes the trace to be routed with a center break instead of a right angle.

■ When held while clicking with the signal-drawing (crosshair) cursor, Ctrl allows a signal to be created without starting from a device pin.

■ When held down while clicking on a device or signal in name mode, Ctrl causes the new name to be created vertically aligned with the previous one.

■ When held down while placing a device or pasting a circuit scrap, Ctrl causes successive items to be placed an equal distance apart. This takes effect only after the second item has been placed. This feature can be used with ⇧ Shift to place a row of devices (see below).

■ Pressing Ctrl disables grid alignment while placing or dragging a name or text item.

■ If held down while using the Set Display Area (right-angle) cursor to zoom in and out, Ctrl prevents the automatic return to point mode.

■ While selecting items in the circuit diagram by clicking on them, pressing Ctrl causes object types to be searched in the opposite order. This can be used, for example, to select a signal name that has accidently moved under a device.

The Alternate Key

Following are various uses of Alt :

■ When held down while clicking on any type of object with the arrow cursor, Alt is equivalent to selecting Set Params with that object selected.

■ When held down while clicking on a device, signal, or pin in name mode, Alt causes a new name to be generated automatically (the last name used with its numeric part incremented). If ⇧ Shift is held down at the same time, the number will be decremented.

■ When held down while drawing a line, Alt causes the vertical and horizontal parts of the right-angle trace to be reversed.

■ While placing a single device or pasting a circuit scrap, pressing Alt prevents any connections from being made to adjacent objects.

■ If pressed before clicking the menu button, Alt allows the Edit Internals menu command to edit PLAs or PROMs, even if they do not have the Allow Reload flag turned on.

■ If pressed while zooming in using the Set Display Area (right-angle) cursor, Alt causes the zoom factor to be set to a maximum of 100% centered around the area selected.

The Shift Key

Following are various uses of ⟨⇧ Shift⟩:

■ Whenever items are being selected, pressing ⟨⇧ Shift⟩ prevents previous items from being deselected. This allows you to select multiple objects for an operation.

■ When held down while drawing a signal, ⟨⇧ Shift⟩ constrains drawing to a single horizontal or vertical line.

■ When held down while placing devices or pasting, ⟨⇧ Shift⟩ constrains mouse movement to be in horizontal or vertical alignment with the previous item.

■ When held down while using the ⟨Alt⟩ auto-naming feature, ⟨⇧ Shift⟩ causes the numeric part of the name to be decremented instead of incremented.

PLA Data File Format

PLA data files contain the names, bit, and pin assignments, as well as product term data. This file can be used to pass device data to LogicWorks for simulation purposes. These files are stored in an ASCII character format, so they can be edited or created externally if necessary. These files are not intended to be user-readable or created without the aid of logic minimization software, so little format checking is done and few error messages are given if the format is not correct. The format is line-oriented, with each input line starting with a keyword followed by associated data. Any line starting with an unrecognized keyword will be ignored, allowing comments or user-defined data to be inserted in the file. The line types are as follows:

FORMAT *formatNum*

This format number is strictly for internal use. It is the PLA file format version number interpreted by LogicWorks for simulation.

TITLE *userName*

The keyword TITLE is followed by one or more blanks, followed by a string specifying the user-assigned name of this device type.

INPUT *name fieldLSB fieldMSB bitOfField nodeName*
    ATTR[*attrKeywords*]

The keyword INPUT is followed by a string giving the name of the field containing this input bit. Following are three numbers giving the bit positions of the least significant and most significant bits of this field and the position of this bit within the field. Bits are numbered from zero being least significant. The fifth item on the line is the name of the node this input bit is assigned to, or blank if no assignment has been made. The last item is the list of attributes for this input, preceded by the keyword ATTR and enclosed in square brackets. Each attribute keyword is selected from an attribute set found in the device entry in the device library. The ATTR item can be omitted completely if no attributes were specified in the source file. All INPUT lines must precede any OUTPUT line.

OUTPUT *name   fieldLSB   fieldMSB   bitOfField   highZ*
    clocked   termType   nodeName ATTR[*attrKeywords*]

The keyword OUTPUT is followed by the name of the output field containing this bit. This is followed by three numbers giving the least and most significant bit numbers assigned to this field and the position of this bit within the field. Bits are numbered from zero starting with the least significant. The next two items are flags (1 = TRUE and 0 = FALSE) indicating the output type. *highZ* tells LogicWorks to create a three-state output in the raw PLA. (This will always be zero in the current version. Enables are handled by the macro mechanism.) *clocked* is 1 if the output receives a clocked assignment, and is not significant in this version. *termType* is an integer specifying the product term types that were written into the file for this output, 1 = low only, 2 = high only, 3 = both types. *nodeName* is the name of the device node assigned to this output bit, and may be null if no node was assigned. The last item is the list of attributes for this output, preceded by the keyword ATTR and enclosed in square brackets. Each attribute keyword is selected from an attribute set found in the device entry in the device library. The ATTR item can be omitted completely if no attributes were specified in the source file.

```
CONTROL  nodeName   ATTR[attrKeywords]
```

The CONTROL line specifies the state of global option fuses. It is a duplicate of the CONTROL statement that appeared in the source file, except that the NODE keyword and its associated brackets have been removed.

```
TERM bitNum type termData
```

The TERM line specifies a product term to be associated with the output bit specified by bitNum. Any number of (zero or more) TERMs may be associated with each OUTPUT. *type* specifies the type of the term, and must be HIGH, LOW, or ENABLE. *termData* consists of N input bit values 0, 1, or X where N is the number of input bits, as indicated by the INPUT lines. The first bit value is for the most significant input bit.

```
END
```

The END line indicates the end of the PLA data file.

PROM Data File Format

PROM data files are defined similarly to PLA data files except that the actual device data is given as a stream of hex data bytes that will be stored in successive memory locations. The hex format is designed to load directly to a PROM programmer.

The file starts with a sequence of INPUT lines, one per input bit, identical to those given for the PLA format. These are followed by a sequence of OUTPUT lines, one per output bit, identical to the PLA format.

The file will contain 1 byte per PROM address if 8 or fewer output bits were specified, or 2 bytes per PROM address if 9 to 16 output bits were specified. The number of addresses in the file will be 2^N where N is the number of input bits. The hex format starts with the keyword HEX on a line by itself. Each subsequent line starts with a colon followed by:

- 2 hex digits (1 byte) indicating the number of actual data bytes on this line

- 4 hex digits (2 bytes) indicating the starting address for the data bytes on this line

■ 2 hex digits which will be "00" in all records, except for an empty terminator record in which they will be "01"

■ groups of 2 digits for the number of data bytes indicated at the beginning of the line

■ 2 hex digits for an 8-bit checksum of all the hex data on the line. The 8-bit sum of all hex data pairs (including count, address, type, data, and checksum) will be 0.

The file is terminated by a hex line with a byte count of 0, address of 0, and type of "01".

Each line of hex should normally contain 16 data bytes, except the last which will contain the remainder.

Glossary

Active-low/Active-high In a PLA, refers to the output level that will be generated when the current input combination matches one of the product terms for a given output bit. An active-high output (AND-OR structure) will be 0 when no term matches and 1 when any term matches. An active-low output (AND-NOR structure) will be the opposite.

Delay A number associated with each device that determines the elapsed time between any input signal value change and the corresponding output change. In LogicWorks this number can be any integer between 0 and 32,767.

Device library A file containing device type definitions. These files are created using the DevEditor module described in Chapter 12, The Device Editor.

Don't Care When used as an input value in a PLA product term, Don't Care means that this input bit does not affect the value of the term.

Don't Know A signal value produced by the simulator when the output value for a device cannot be determined, due to a Don't Know or unconnected input.

Enable Refers to the controlling input to a three-state output device. When an output is enabled, it is driving its pin to either a 0 or 1 level.

High Impedance Refers to an output state in which output drivers are turned off and the device is not affecting the attached signal line.

Macro device A device read from a library whose simulation characteristics are determined by an internal LogicWorks circuit. These devices are created using the DevEditor module.

Page Connector   This is a special type of device symbol that allows a logical signal connection to be made between circuit pages. Any signal with a Page Connector attached will be logically connected to any like-named signal on another page that also has a Page Connector attached. Multipage schematics are not supported in LogicWorks, but these devices are provided for upward compatibility with DesignWorks.

PLA (Programmable Logic Array)   Can be used generally to refer to a programmable logic device, but is used in this manual specifically to refer to devices having an AND-OR structure with programmable connections between the input lines and the AND array.

Polarity   In a PLA, refers to the output structure of a given pin. If an output is inverted (as in the AND-NOR structure) it is said to have active-low polarity. If it is non-inverted, it is active-high.

Primitive device   A device from the Gates, Generic, or I/O libraries. The logic characteristics of these devices are determined by program code internal to LogicWorks.

PROM (Programmable Read Only Memory)   A read-only storage device that can be programmed by the user. Has N input lines, M output lines, and 2^N internal storage locations each containing M bits. The programmable connections exist between the AND gates and the outputs.

Signal Connector   A special type of device which causes the attached signal to become logically connected to all other signals having a like-named Signal Connector device attached. This is different from a Page Connector in that it forces a specific name onto the attached signal line.

Term/product term/AND term   Used synonymously in LogicWorks to refer to a single AND group in an AND-OR logic structure. For example, A AND B AND NOT C is one term, since it can be implemented with one AND gate. For notational convenience, terms are usually written in 01X format, where 0 refers to an inverted input, 1 refers to a non-inverted input, and X refers to a Don't Care input (that is, not used in this term). If the circuit in question had 5 inputs, A, B, C, D, and E, the above term might be written 110XX.

Three-state   Refers to a device output that can be placed in a High Impedance state (no output drive).

Index

Other Products
for Circuit Design
from Capilano Computing

Capilano Computing sells a complete line of tools for computer and electronic engineering students and professionals. This section describes some of these products and how they can be used with LogicWorks for teaching and professional circuit-design applications.

Special pricing is available for educational institutions.

FREE OFFER: See special *free* and low-cost offers for LogicWorks owners on the registration card enclosed with the disks.

LogicWorks Extended Libraries

This set of symbol libraries gives you hundreds of standard chip types for use with LogicWorks.™ Included are more than 350 devices from the 7400 series, plus many CMOS and ECL devices. Every symbol has full internal logic simulation.

Available for the Apple Macintosh and PC-compatible computers.

The LogicBox™

Hardware Experiment Interface

What is the LogicBox?

The LogicBox is a hardware interface unit that links LogicWorks to a real digital experiment. Simulated signals in a circuit diagram are converted to real pulses at the outputs of the LogicBox. Similarly, signal-value changes in the real digital circuit can be converted to logic levels in the simulated circuit on the screen.

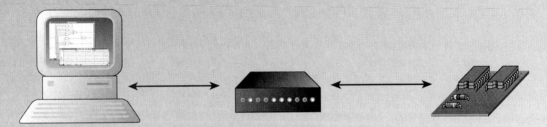

| Use all the simulation and display features of LogicWorks to control and monitor your experiment on the screen. | The LogicBox has 32 I/O lines that can either drive or monitor a signal in your experiment. High-impedance detection ability makes it easy to locate wiring errors. | The LogicBox can replace expensive and damage-prone meters, probes, and oscilloscopes for low-speed experiments. |

LogicBox Specifications

Computer interface: Serial port, 9,600/56K baud

Experiment interface: 32 individually programmable I/O lines

TTL levels

$2 \times$ LSTTL loads

Available for the Apple Macintosh and PC-compatible computers.

DesignWorks™

Professional Schematic Capture

DesignWorks is a full schematic capture and digital simulation system for professional applications. DesignWorks has the same ease of use and interactive style as LogicWorks, but with many additional features, including:

- Device symbol libraries with over 13,000 parts
- Automatic assignment of gates to packages
- Bussing
- Multiple pages per circuit
- Fully hierarchical design
- Many additional editing features
- Configurable netlist and report generator
- Special support for PCB, SPICE, FPGA, and VLSI designs
- Circuit files created by LogicWorks can be read by DesignWorks

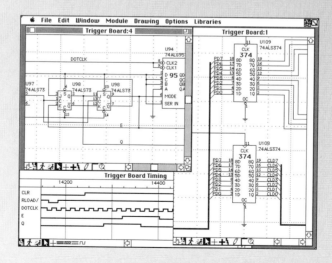

DesignWorks is available for the Apple Macintosh and Microsoft Windows.

ABEL™ Student Edition

PLD Compiler

ABEL Student Edition is a system for designing circuits with Programmable Logic Devices, such as PAL™ devices. You describe your circuit as a set of Boolean equations, state diagrams or truth tables, or any combination of the three. ABEL automatically minimizes the logic and produces a "fuse map" file that can be used to program a device. Designs that used to take numerous standard chips can now be squeezed into a single chip. In addition, you can describe your design using high-level concepts instead of gates and flip-flops.

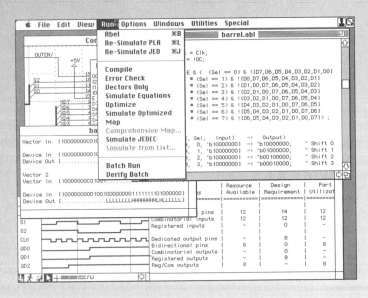

ABEL can be used with DesignWorks or LogicWorks to simulate your complete design before programming any devices. A design created using ABEL becomes a single device symbol on the schematic diagram. Any number of these PLD symbols can be combined with standard logic devices to verify your complete design.

ABEL Student Edition is based on the industry-standard ABEL™ (Advanced Boolean Expression Language) package from Data I/O Corporation, but with restricted device support and no OPEN-ABEL module capability.

Available for the Apple Macintosh and PC compatibles. Also available from Capilano Computing is the MacABEL™ full professional version with extensive industry device support.

MEDA™ Developer's Kit

Custom Programming Interface

The MEDA™ (Modular Electronic Design Application™) interface allows users to implement add-on functions for DesignWorks™ or LogicWorks. External code modules can interrogate or modify any schematic or simulation data in memory, and the module can respond to many types of simulation events or user actions. Add-on functions implemented in a MEDA module are completely integrated with the program and appear to the user like built-in functions.

MEDA can be used to implement specialized and highly inter-active circuit design tools without having to develop a complete application from scratch. MEDA has been successfully used to implement file I/O, behavioral device models, interactive display panels, alternate circuit views, and other functions. Other potential applications include:

- A complete, new simulation module, such as analog circuit simulation

- Control of external instrumentation, such as logic analyzers, oscilloscopes, pattern generators, and more

- Interfaces to external simulation hardware

- Various types of circuit analysis, such as timing analysis and fault analysis

- Interactive rule checking

MEDA modules can be written in standard C language in the MPW™ (Macintosh Programmer's Workbench) or ThinkC™ environment and can take advantage of any standard Macintosh™ graphics features such as windows, menus, and controls. Modules are compiled completely independently of DesignWorks and require no installation other than simply placing the module file on the user's disk.

Available for the Apple Macintosh only.

Other Products

A variety of other circuit design products are available from Capilano Computing, including:

- Analog simulation
- Printed circuit board layout
- Radio frequency design

Please call or write for up-to-date information.

Educators and professors: Call us for special pricing on all our professional circuit design products.

PLEASE NOTE: New products are being added and existing products enhanced on a continuous basis. The specifications given here are intended only as an outline of general capabilities and do not represent a commitment by Capilano Computing.

Please contact us for the latest product information and prices.

Call toll-free: **1-800-444-9064** (U.S. only) or (604) 522-6200

Fax: (604) 522-3972

Capilano
Computing

Registration Form

Name _____

School or college _____

Address _____

_____

City _____

State/Province _____ ZIP/Postal Code _____

Phone (optional) AREA CODE _____ NUMBER _____

Fax or E-Mail (optional) AREA CODE _____ NUMBER _____

Where did you purchase LogicWorks? _____

Computer make and model _____ Memory _____

Owner is: ☐ Student ☐ Instructor ☐ College/University/Technical School

☐ Business ☐ Other _____

Comments on LogicWorks: _____

_____

*Please enclose this registration form
and check (if applicable) and mail to:*

Capilano
Computing
Post Office Box 775
Pleasanton, CA 94566-0077

Registration Form

SPECIAL OFFERS TO LOGICWORKS OWNERS!

Complete both sides of this form and return it to register your copy of LogicWorks and receive a **FREE Extras disk**. While you're at it, make your LogicWorks even more useful by purchasing some add-on products at extremely low student prices. Allow 4–6 weeks for delivery. Please feel free to add any comments about LogicWorks on this form or on a separate page.

☐ **YES!** Please send my *free* Extras diskette for LogicWorks™ with more symbol libraries and sample circuits .... **FREE!**

☐ **YES!** Please send the LogicWorks™ 7400 & 4000 Libraries— More than 350 symbols with complete simulation for standard 7400 series TTL devices and 4000 series CMOS device **$19.95**

☐ **YES!** Please send the LogicWorks™ Microprocessor Libraries— Symbols with bus cycle simulation for 6809, 6809E, 68000, 68020, 68030, 68HC11, 8031, 8051, 8751, 8086, and 8088 ....**$19.95**

☐ **YES!** Please send the ABEL™ Student Edition—Describe circuits in a high-level language and simulate them in LogicWorks **$39.95**

Total amount of purchase... **$.**

All prices are in U.S. dollars and include shipping, handling, and local taxes, where applicable.

☐ Macintosh (3½" 800K diskette)   ☐ DOS (3½" 1.4mB diskette)

☐ Check enclosed *(please make payable to Capilano Computing)*

☐ Visa/MC/AmEx number _____ Exp. date_____

Signature (credit cards only) _____